MACMILLAN

UPPER L

WILLIAM SHAKESPEARE

Macbeth

Retold by Margaret Tarner

MACMILLAN

MACMILLAN READERS

UPPER LEVEL

Founding Editor: John Milne

The Macmillan Readers provide a choice of enjoyable reading materials for learners of English. The series is published at six levels – Starter, Beginner, Elementary, Pre-intermediate, Intermediate and Upper.

Level Control
Information, structure and vocabulary are controlled to suit the students' ability at each level.

The number of words at each level:

Starter	about 300 basic words
Beginner	about 600 basic words
Elementary	about 1100 basic words
Pre-intermediate	about 1400 basic words
Intermediate	about 1600 basic words
Upper	about 2200 basic words

Vocabulary
Some difficult words and phrases in this book are important for understanding the story. Some of these words are explained in the story, some are shown in the pictures, and others are marked with a number like this: ...[3]. Words with a number are explained in the *Glossary* at the end of the book.

Answer Keys
Answer Keys for the *Points for Understanding* and *Exercises* sections can be found at www.macmillanenglish.com/readers.

Audio Download
There is an audio download available to buy for this title. Visit www.macmillanenglish.com/readers for more information.

Contents

Contents (continued ...)

A Note About The Author

William Shakespeare was born in April 1564 in Stratford-upon-Avon, a busy market town about eighty miles north-west of London. His father, John Shakespeare, was a businessman who made gloves and also bought and sold wool. William was given a good education at the local school, where he learnt Latin and studied literature. He would have read many great classical works, and his knowledge of these can be seen in his plays.

Shakespeare's father was not a very successful businessman. He fell into debt and there was not enough money for William to go to university. In 1582, William married Ann Hathaway, who was eight years older than her young husband. The couple had a daughter and, later, twins. Very little else is known about Shakespeare's early life after his marriage.

However, we do know that by 1592, Shakespeare was living in London, working as an actor and writing plays. This would have been an interesting time for the young playwright. There were about 200 000 people living in London, and there were only four or five theatres for them to visit. These theatres would have been different from modern ones. They were usually round or eight-sided buildings, and they held about 3000 people. The audience stood around three sides of the stage and there was no roof over the central part of the theatre, so neither the audience nor the actors had protection from the weather. Plays were acted in the afternoons and if it rained, nearly everyone used to get wet. Richer people could pay for better seats, which were under cover. At the back of the main stage, there were two balconies – one for the musicians and one for the actors. The space under the balconies was part of the stage, but could be separated from it by a curtain. The actors walked onto the main stage through two doors at the back.

Sometimes six different plays were performed by a company in one week, so there was a constant demand for new plays. A clever playwright could make old plays into new ones by adding characters, writing new speeches and even changing the story. Shakespeare became very good at doing this. He worked very fast and knew just what the audience wanted. He knew how to frighten people and how to make them laugh or cry, so his plays became very popular.

Londoners could be influenced[1] by the plays they watched, so Shakespeare had to be very careful when he wrote them. His manuscripts[2] were always checked by a court official to prevent any treason[3] being written against Queen Elizabeth I and later against King James.

Shakespeare's name soon became very well-known. Some playwrights were jealous of his success. Some laughed at him because he had never been to university, but others respected him and became his friends. By about 1613 he retired[4] and returned to Stratford where he had bought a house. He lived there with his family until his death in 1616.

All the theatres where Shakespeare worked, including the Globe where his most famous plays were performed, were destroyed long ago. But there is now a new Globe on the South Bank of the River Thames. There you can see Shakespeare's plays performed just as they were in his lifetime. It is an exciting experience.

A Note About This Play

Macbeth is the last of Shakespeare's tragedies and also the shortest. A tragedy is a play in which the most important characters die or end their lives unhappily. These people are often royal figures who, because of some fault in their character, may be partly responsible for their fate[5]. Shakespeare wrote *Macbeth* between 1606 and 1607. As is typical with playwrights' work from this period, there are several versions of the play, which was not published until 1623.

Shakespeare wrote the play during a time of great political unrest[6] in England. Queen Elizabeth I had died in 1603 and King James of Scotland had become King James I of England. James believed that he had been chosen by God to rule England. However, many people wanted a Catholic king on the throne[7], and in 1605, an attempt was made to kill the King and all the members of his parliament[8]. The plot failed and its leaders were executed[9]. King James was safe, but it had been a frightening time for everyone. These events gave Shakespeare the idea for a new play.

King James enjoyed watching plays and he had given Shakespeare's acting company the new name of The King's Men. The company continued to perform at the Globe Theatre, but the King invited them to his court too. A new play would have to please and flatter[10] the King.

Shakespeare got the idea for *Macbeth* from a true story about Scotland. It was about the murder of a king, so Shakespeare had to be careful. He had to make it clear how terrible the murder was and show how the murderers were punished.

As usual, he changed parts of the story and added his own ideas to make it more interesting to his audience and, of course, to the King himself. For example, one of the main characters, Banquo, is an ancestor of King James. In the original story, Banquo helped to murder the King. In Shakespeare's version, Banquo is horrified by the murder and becomes Macbeth's enemy.

At the beginning of the play, Macbeth himself is shown to be a brave soldier, who is loved and honoured by old King Duncan. By the end of the play, Macbeth has become a tyrant[11], and is hated and feared by everyone. How does this happen? The answer is partly to be found in the character of Macbeth himself. His greatest ambition is to be King and so when supernatural[12] powers – the three witches – tell him that he will rule Scotland, he believes them.

Macbeth is encouraged by his wife, Lady Macbeth, whose ambitions[13] are as strong as her husband's. In spite of Macbeth's fears she persuades him to kill King Duncan with her help. Macbeth is made King, but one murder leads to another, and a dreadful[14] story of death and unhappiness follows.

Macbeth goes back to ask the three witches more about his future. Their answers seem to tell him that he will never be defeated, but Macbeth realizes, too late, that he has been tricked.

Macbeth is more than just an ambitious but cruel soldier. He also has a powerful imagination and is able to see the consequences of his actions. At first, Macbeth is greatly influenced by his more practical wife. But later, he decides to act alone, and Lady Macbeth is finally destroyed by her own wickedness.

The Supernatural

Many people want to know what will happen to them in the future. Some people think that the stars will tell them. Others visit those who claim to have special powers. If something we are told about the future comes true, we are more likely to believe everything else we are told.

In Shakespeare's time, many people believed in the power of witches. Witches were usually women who were thought to foretell[15] the future by using magic powers. Sometimes they behaved badly towards people they did not like. They might put a spell[16] on these people so that they or their families would be harmed. This was called *witchcraft*.

King James himself was interested in witchcraft and he had written a book about witches. So the supernatural is important in the play. The three witches, or 'all-seeing sisters', tell Macbeth and Banquo what will happen to them. Macbeth, who is imaginative and ambitious, is quick to believe them.

The witches say and do many strange things. This made the play popular with the King and with the Londoners who saw the play at the Globe. Modern audiences enjoy the witches too, and they still have the power to interest and even frighten us.

Shakespeare's Language

Shakespeare, like other playwrights of his time, wrote his plays in a kind of poetry called *blank verse*. Blank verse does not rhyme, but each line usually has five weak and five strong beats. It is very important that the strong beat falls on the stressed part of a word.

Macbeth is mostly written in blank verse. Here is an example, in Shakespeare's own words, which shows the strong and weak beats:

□ ☐ □ ☐ □ ☐ □ ☐ □ ☐
Lady Macbeth: This **is** the **very painting of** your **fear:**

□ ☐ □ ☐ □ ☐ □ ☐ □ ☐
This **is** the **air**-drawn **dagger, which,** you **said,**

□ ☐ □ ☐ □ ☐ □ ☐ □ ☐
Led **you** to **Dun**can. **O,** these **flaws** and **starts**

□ ☐ □ ☐ □ ☐ □ ☐ □ ☐
(Imposters **to** true **fear**) would **well** become

□ ☐ □ ☐ □ ☐ □ ☐ □ ☐
A **wom**an's **story at** a **winter's fire.**

However, not all the lines in *Macbeth* are as regular as this. Shakespeare sometimes chooses to use shorter lines to show that the speaker is angry or afraid.

Macbeth: The table's full.
Lennox: Here is a place reserved, sir.
Macbeth: Where?
Lennox: Here, my good lord … What is it that moves your highness?
Macbeth: Which of you have done this?
Lord: What, my good lord?
Macbeth: Thou canst not say I did it: never shake
Thy gory locks at me.

Some speeches in *Macbeth* include the use of *rhyming couplets* – pairs of lines in which the last word of the first line rhymes with the last word of the second. A sense of drama and magic is created when the witches speak by the use of rhyming couplets.

1st Witch: When shall we three meet again?
In thunder, lightning, or in rain?
2nd Witch: When the hurly-burly's done,
When the battle's lost, and won.
3rd Witch: That will be ere the set of sun.

A single rhyming couplet is also often used by other characters to add a dramatic end to a scene.

Malcolm: Receive what cheer[17] you may:
The night is long that never finds the day.

For more information about William Shakespeare, including projects and webquests, visit the student's section of the Macmillan Readers website at www.macmillanenglish.com/readers. There you can also find an interview with Michael Maloney, who plays Macbeth, and profiles of the other actors who star in the audio version of this Macmillan Reader.

This Version Of Macbeth

This Macmillan Reader includes some short extracts from Shakespeare's own version of *Macbeth*. The extracts follow immediately after their simplified form. They are shaded in grey and have a separate glossary. In the glossary, words that are not used in modern English appear in *italics*. See the example (from pages 16–18) below:

Banquo: Tell me the truth, you creatures.
Are you old women, as you seem to be,
Or are you not real at all?
You've told Macbeth his present and his future fate,
And that has left him silent.
If you have knowledge of the seeds of time –
Which seeds will grow and which will not, then tell me now.

Banquo: *I'th'* name of truth,
Are *ye fantastical*, or that indeed
Which *outwardly ye* show? My noble partner
You greet with present grace and great prediction
Of noble having and of royal hope,
That he seems *wrapt withall*: to me *you* speak not.
If you can look into the seeds of time,
And say which grain will grow and which will not,
Speak then to me, who neither beg nor fear
Your favours nor your hate.

simplified text

original text

ye = you
fantastical = of the imagination
outwardly = on the outside
present grace = honour given at this time
prediction = a statement about what the future will be
wrapt withal = very deep in thought
grain = a seed

glossary

The People In This Story

Duncan – the King of Scotland

Malcolm

Donalbain } Duncan's sons

Macbeth

Banquo } generals of the King's army

Macduff

Ross

Angus } thanes[18] of Scotland

Lennox

Menteith

Lady Macbeth – Macbeth's wife

Lady Macduff – Macduff's wife

Boy – Macduff and Lady Macduff's young son

Fleance – Banquo's son

Siward – general of the English army

Young Siward – Siward's son

Seyton – a soldier who looks after Macbeth

Three witches – all-seeing sisters who can foretell the future

Two murderers

A captain, a doctor, a porter, soldiers, servants and messengers

Act 1, Scene 1

[Thunder and lightning. Out of the foggy air come three ugly old women, dressed in black. They are witches]
1st Witch: When shall we three meet again,
In thunder, lightning, or in rain?
2nd Witch: When the fighting is all done,
When the battle's lost and won.
3rd Witch: Before night covers everyone.
1st Witch: Where's the place?
2nd Witch: Upon the heath[19].
3rd Witch: There to meet with Macbeth!
All Witches: Fair is foul[20] and foul is fair,
Flying through the dark and foggy air!
[They laugh and disappear into the fog]

Act 1, Scene 2

[King Duncan and some thanes at a camp, some distance from the battle. Enter Malcolm, the King's eldest son, with a wounded soldier]
Duncan: Who is that poor man? His wounds are bleeding.
Surely he can tell us how the battle's going.
Malcolm: This is the captain, who by his bravery,
Saved me from certain death.
Duncan: Welcome, brave friend! Tell me all you know.
How was the battle going when you had to leave?
Captain: For a long time, it was still in doubt.
The rebel[21] force was strong – their men fought well.
Then brave Macbeth – for brave he surely is,
Fought till he reached the rebels' wicked[22] leader.
Then, bloody sword in hand, he faced the traitor[23]
And with one blow[24], cut him almost in two.
And put the traitor's head upon our castle wall,

Where all can see it and be glad.

Duncan: Oh, brave Macbeth, what a great man he is!

Captain: The battle was not over, King of Scotland.
Some rebels turned and ran, but others came.
Fresh soldiers then began to fight against us.

Duncan: And were not Macbeth – and Banquo too,
Alarmed[25] by this?

Captain: Are lions alarmed by hares[26]?
Our two great thanes began to fight fiercely.
With their strong swords they cut and cut again.
... But help me sir, my wounds are deep, I bleed ...

Duncan: Rest now, brave man, you have said enough.
Look after him. He must not lose more blood.
[The captain is taken away. Enter the Thane of Ross]
Here is more news. What do you know, good thane?

Ross: I come from Fife, my gracious[27] King,
Where the great King of Norway fought against us,
Assisted[28] by the rebel Thane of Cawdor.
But do not fear, my lord, our leader, great Macbeth
Took on the fight and won. The victory was ours.
And the defeated King of Norway begged for peace.

Duncan: Great happiness!
But how the Thane of Cawdor has deceived us!
That rebel thane shall have a traitor's death.
The Thane of Cawdor is now brave Macbeth.

Act 1, Scene 3

[On a foggy heath. The sound of thunder. Enter the three witches]
1ˢᵗ Witch: Where have you been, sister?
2ⁿᵈ Witch: Killing pigs.
3ʳᵈ Witch: And what about you, sister?
1ˢᵗ Witch: A greedy sailor's wife was eating nuts.
She chewed and chewed and chewed.
'Give some to me,' I said.
'Leave me alone, you dirty witch!' she cried.
Her husband is at sea – his ship is called the *Tiger*.
I'll call for a strong wind and follow him.
2ⁿᵈ Witch: I'll give you a wind.
1ˢᵗ Witch: You are kind.
3ʳᵈ Witch: And I another.
1ˢᵗ Witch: And I myself have all the other.
I'll blow him east and blow him west,
But never will that man be blest[29].
He will not sleep by night or day.
Never will he find his way,
To friendly port or place of rest.
Look what I have!
2ⁿᵈ Witch: Show me, show me.
1ˢᵗ Witch: Look, another sailor's thumb.
He drowned[30] as homeward[31] he did come.
[The sound of a drum]
3ʳᵈ Witch: A drum I hear.
Macbeth is near!
[The three witches hold hands and dance in a circle]
All Witches: We three sisters, hand in hand.
Travel over sea and land.
Left we go and right we turn,
Three times your way, three times mine,
Three times more to make it nine.

Quiet now. Our spell is made.

[The witches disappear into the fog. Enter Macbeth and Banquo]

Macbeth: The weather goes from foul to fair.

This dirty fog darkens the clear air.

Banquo: How far are we from Forres?

[The fog clears and he sees the three witches]

Who are these old creatures, dressed in dirty clothes?

They must be women, though I can't believe it.

You seem to understand me, but you're silent.

Macbeth: Speak, if you can. Who are you?

1st Witch: All hail[32], Macbeth. Hail to you, Thane of Glamis!

2nd Witch: All hail, Macbeth. Hail to you, Thane of Cawdor!

3rd Witch: All hail, Macbeth. You will be King of Scotland!

Banquo: *[To Macbeth]* Why do you seem to fear a future full of promise?

[Turning to the witches]

Tell me the truth, you creatures.

Are you old women, as you seem to be,

Or are you not real at all?

You've told Macbeth his present and his future fate,

And that has left him silent.

If you have knowledge of the seeds of time –

Which seeds will grow and which will not, then tell me now.

Banquo: I'th' name of truth,

Are ye fantastical, or that indeed

Which outwardly ye show? My noble partner

You greet with present grace and great prediction

Of noble having and of royal hope,

That he seems wrapt withall: to me you speak not.

If you can look into the seeds of time,

And say which grain will grow and which will not,

Speak then to me, who neither beg nor fear

Your favours nor your hate.

16

Who are these old creatures, dressed in dirty clothes?
They must be women, though I can't believe it.

ye = you
fantastical = of the imagination
outwardly = on the outside
present grace = honour given at this time
prediction = a statement about what the future will be
wrapt withal = very deep in thought
grain = a seed

1st Witch: Hail!

2nd Witch: Hail!

3rd Witch: Hail!

1st Witch: You are lesser than Macbeth, but greater.

2nd Witch: Not so happy, but much happier.

3rd Witch: *[to Banquo]* You'll not be King, but you will father kings.

So all hail, Macbeth and Banquo!

1st Witch: Banquo and Macbeth, all hail!

[The fog gets thicker]

Macbeth: Wait! You have not said enough. I must know more.

My father's death has made me Thane of Glamis.

But Thane of Cawdor? No, that's wrong.

The Thane of Cawdor is alive and well.

And as for being King, that is impossible.

Tell me where you got your knowledge from

And how you know my future.

Stay, tell me more – I order you!

[The witches laugh and disappear into the fog]

Banquo: The fog has hidden them.

Where have they gone?

Macbeth: Into the air. I wish they had stayed.

Banquo: Were they really here or are we mad?

Macbeth: They said your children will be kings.

Banquo: You shall be King. They said that too.

Macbeth: And Thane of Cawdor. Isn't that right?

Banquo: That's exactly what they said.

[Enter two thanes, Ross and Angus]

Who's this?

Ross: The King knows of your courage, brave Macbeth.

He has had news of it from every side.

Angus: We have both come to bring our royal master's thanks

And take you to him, for he wants to see you.

And, from the King, we bring a further honour.

You have been named 'Macbeth, the Thane of Cawdor'.

Banquo: That's what the witches said. How did they know?

Can they foretell the future?

Macbeth: The Thane of Cawdor is alive. Why give me his title?

Ross: The Thane's alive, that's true, but he's a traitor.

And very soon, he'll die a traitor's death.

Macbeth: *[Speaking to himself]* Glamis and Cawdor ...

That's what the witches said. The best is still to come.

[To Angus]

Thank you, kind sir.

[To Banquo]

Now you must hope your children will be kings.

They've told the truth to me. Why not to you?

Banquo: If you believe that, you must believe

That one day, you'll be King. I am not happy.

These things of darkness may have come to trick us,

Tell us some truths, but lead us into evil.

[To Ross and Angus]

Good friends, I must speak to you a minute.

Macbeth: *[To himself]*

The witches said two things about me – both were true.

That surely means that one day I'll be King.

They all foretold my future – is that good or bad?

If bad, why did the witches give me hope?

They called me Thane of Cawdor – now I am.

So other truths may follow. If good,

Why am I thinking of a plan – a terrible idea,

That frightens me so much, that my hair stands on end?
And my heart, too, is beating far too fast.
But yet the dreadful fears that I have now,
Are nothing to the deadly horrors in my mind.
My body and my mind are so confused,
That action itself, gives way to wildest thoughts.
Imagination has replaced reality.

Macbeth: *If ill, why hath it given me earnest of success,*
Commencing in a truth? I am Thane of Cawdor:
If good, why do I yield to that suggestion
Whose horrid image doth unfix my hair,
And make my seated heart knock at my ribs,
Against the use of Nature? Present fears
Are less than horrible imaginings:
My thought, whose murder yet is but fantastical,
Shakes so my single state of man,
That function is smother'd in surmise,
And nothing is, but what is not.

hath = has
earnest = very serious information
commencing = starting
yield = give in or surrender
doth = does
unfix = stand on end
seated = fixed
function = power to act
smother'd = covered thickly, with too much of something
surmise = strange ideas

Banquo: Our friend is deep in thought. Something is troubling him.
Macbeth: *[Continuing to himself]* If fate will make me King,
Then fate will crown[33] me. I do not need to act.
Banquo: Macbeth's new honours are too much for him.

Macbeth: *[Still to himself]* Whatever happens, come what may,
Time will go on, to end the strangest day.
Banquo: Worthy[34] Macbeth, are you ready now?
Macbeth: *[To Banquo]* I'm coming, sir.
I'm sorry, friends, my thoughts have been confused.
Gentlemen, I thank you. Let's go to the King.
[To Banquo]
I want to speak to you about the witches,
And what they told us.
We must be honest with each other.
Banquo: Indeed we must.
Macbeth: Then we'll talk later.
[To Ross and Angus]
Come, friends, take us to the King.

Act 1, Scene 4

[Inside King Duncan's palace]
Duncan: Is the wicked traitor Cawdor dead?
Malcolm: My lord, he is.
Before he died, he asked for your forgiveness.
And he confessed[35] his treason.
He died more nobly[36] than he lived. He smiled.
Life had no more meaning left for him.
Duncan: There is no way to learn another's thoughts.
His face was honest and I trusted him.
[Enter Macbeth, Banquo, Ross and Angus]
My dear Macbeth, I owe you much,
Much more than I can ever pay you.
You deserve all that I have and more.
Macbeth: I am your subject and I owe you service.
You are the King and you deserve our duty[37].
That duty is our pleasure and all our deeds[38]
Show love and honour to you.
Duncan: You are welcome here and as time passes
Our friendship will grow stronger.
And noble Banquo, you too deserve our thanks –
All men must know it. I hold you in my arms,
Near to my heart.
Banquo: My love will grow with yours.
Duncan: I am so happy – tears are not far away.
Sons, cousins, thanes, I want you all to know
That Malcolm, my dear eldest son, will be my heir[39].
He will be made the Prince of Cumberland
At Inverness, where others will receive new honours.
Let us go there together.
Macbeth: I'll go ahead and tell my wife you're coming.
She must prepare our castle for your visit.
Duncan: Thank you, worthy Cawdor.

Macbeth: *[To himself]*
The Prince of Cumberland! So Malcolm will be King.
The boy stands in my way. I must act quickly.
Or not act at all.
You stars above, no longer shine!
Black skies must hide these black thoughts of mine.
I must do that foul deed that I dare not see.
Yes, I will do it. What will be, will be.

Act 1, Scene 5

[Macbeth's castle, at Inverness in Scotland. Enter Lady Macbeth, reading a letter from her husband]

Lady Macbeth: 'These all-seeing sisters met me on the day of victory. Since then, I have found out more about them. They have strange powers. Then came messengers from the King. They called me Thane of Cawdor, just as the witches had. But the three sisters had told me something else. They said I would be the future King! My dearest partner, their promise will make you Queen. Think of our great joy to come. Farewell.'

[She speaks to herself]

You are Glamis and Cawdor too. And you shall be
What the three sisters promised. But yet I fear
You do not have the will to get what you desire[40].
You are ambitious, but not bold[41] enough
To do what must be done. To get the crown,
You must commit a murder, and you know it.
You must do wrong, but fear to do that wrong.
Husband, come quickly, so that my bolder spirit
Will help you put aside all that still keeps you
From the golden crown that fate says shall be yours.

[Enter servant]

What is your news?

Servant: The King comes here tonight.

Lady Macbeth: The King? You are mad to call your master that.

[Quickly correcting herself]

I mean … the King is with your master.
King Duncan is our guest tonight.

Servant: Yes, my lady.

Lady Macbeth: This is good news, but there is much to do.
Go, we must be ready for the King.

[Exit servant. Lady Macbeth to herself]

That black bird, the raven, with his cry,

Both warns and welcomes Duncan to my castle,
Come to me, you spirits, who are always waiting,
Ready to put black thoughts in human minds!
Take womanly weakness from me – make me like a man!
Fill me from top to toe with hellish cruelty.
Strengthen my powers, weaken all thoughts of pity.
Silence my conscience, so that no guilty feelings
Prevent my foul plan having the end I wish for!

Lady Macbeth: *The raven himself is hoarse,*
That croaks the fatal entrance of Duncan
Under my battlements. Come, you spirits
That tend on mortal thoughts, unsex me here,
And fill me, from the crown to the toe, top-full
Of direst cruelty! Make thick my blood,
Stop up th'access and passage to remorse,
That no compunctious visitings of nature
Shake my fell purpose, nor keep peace between
Th'effect and it!

hoarse = with a dry, rough throat
croaks = makes a rough-sounding noise
battlements = the very top of the castle wall
tend = attend, look after
mortal thoughts = the thoughts of humans
crown = top of the head
direst = most dreadful
remorse = pity
compunctious = from her conscience
fell = cruel

[*She continues*] Come, darkest night and grow darker yet,
So my sharp knife sees not the wound it makes.
Cover the eyes of Heaven as I do the dreadful deed!
[*Enter Macbeth*]
Great Glamis! Worthy Cawdor! Greater than both
As the three sisters promised! Your letter's taken me

Great Glamis! Worthy Cawdor! Greater than both
As the three sisters promised!

From present time to future glory[42] in a moment!

Macbeth: My dearest love, Duncan comes here tonight.

Lady Macbeth: When does he leave?

Macbeth: Tomorrow – that is his plan.

Lady Macbeth: Tomorrow? No. Duncan will never see tomorrow.
Your face is like a book, my dearest lord,
Where men can read strange things.
Your looks, your actions, all must welcome him.
Our wicked purpose must be kept well hidden.
You can trust me to carry out this business.
Then all our days and nights to come will be
Strong with the power that goes with royalty.

Macbeth: We need to talk more …

Lady Macbeth: The way ahead is clear.
I tell you we have nothing else to fear.
Leave all the rest to me.

[Exit Macbeth and Lady Macbeth]

Act 1, Scene 6

[Outside Macbeth's castle. Enter King Duncan with his sons, Malcolm and Donalbain, and also Banquo, Lennox and Ross]

Duncan: What a pleasant place! The air is sweet and fresh.

Banquo: Birds nesting here sing their sweetest songs,

And give us a cheerful welcome.

[Enter Lady Macbeth]

Duncan: Here's our honoured hostess[43], with her welcome too!

Madam, I ask you to forgive me for the trouble

That my royal visit gives you.

Lady Macbeth: Nothing we can do to serve you is enough.

Our thanks and welcome should be doubled

And doubled yet again.

And in return for honours given to us

We offer up our prayers for your safety.

Duncan: Where is the Thane of Cawdor?

We followed him, but could not overtake him.

His love for you brought him here before us.

Fair and noble hostess, we are your guests tonight.

Lady Macbeth: Dear sir, all we have belongs to you.

We still owe you more than we can pay.

Duncan: Give me your hand and take me to Macbeth.

We love him well and know we always will.

Let us go in together, my dear hostess.

Act 1, Scene 7

[Outside the great hall of Macbeth's castle later the same day. The feast[44] in honour of the King has begun and the guests are enjoying their meal. Macbeth has left the hall to think about the murder he and his wife have planned]

Macbeth: If I do it, then I must do it quickly.
But will this murder be enough? Will it bring success?
Or will more problems follow?
No man avoids the judgment that's to come
And I'll be judged in this world too.
For murderous deeds may lead to other murders.
If one king dies, then others may die too.
The crown won't make me safe from quick revenge[45].
And there's another thing that troubles me …
King Duncan trusts me and for two good reasons.
First, I am his cousin and his subject too.
And so I owe him loyalty. That is his right.
There's a second point. I am his host.
I should protect him, keep him from all harm,
And not harm him myself.
Duncan has been a gracious king, he has ruled wisely.
His noble deeds will plead[46] with angelic[47] voices
Against the horror of his dreadful death.
And pity, helpless as a new-born child, will take on
Heaven's power. The whole world will know of it.
The storm of all men's anger will be turned to tears.
Ambition is my only spur[48] and that may be my downfall.
[Enter Lady Macbeth]
What's happening now? Has Duncan asked for me?
Lady Macbeth: Of course he has. The feast is almost over.
Why did you leave the hall?
Macbeth: I had to think. We'll go no further with our plan.

Duncan has honoured me and all men praise[49] me.
I do not wish to lose their good opinions.
Lady Macbeth: *[Impatiently]* Were you drunk when you spoke to me before?
Are you a coward[50] after all, afraid to act?
I cannot and I will not love a coward.
The crown is what you want – are you afraid to take it?
The golden crown of Scotland can be yours.
But cowardly fear has killed your deep desire.
Macbeth: Be quiet! I dare do anything a brave man will do.
Who dares do more, is not a man at all.
Lady Macbeth: What beast was it then that first told me the plan?
When you dared do it, then you were a man.
All that you needed were the right time and place.
Now Duncan's here. Will there be a better time than this?
Is that what frightens you? … Listen to me.
I have had a child and watched it drink my milk.
I would have killed it, as it smiled at me,
Rather than break my word, as you have done.
Macbeth: But what if we fail?
Lady Macbeth: Use all your courage and we cannot fail.
Duncan will be tired, after the long day's journey.
As soon as he's asleep, I'll give his servants wine.
They will sleep too and remember nothing.
How easy it will be then for us to do the deed,
For which they will be blamed!
Macbeth: All your future children should be boys!
There is nothing of the woman in your nature.
I'll use the servants' daggers[51].
I'll cover both the sleeping men with blood.
There'll be no doubt about who killed the King.
Lady Macbeth: When everyone has heard our cries of grief[52],

Who will dare blame us?
Macbeth: My mind's made up. Every part of me is ready
To do the awful deed.
False, smiling faces must be what we show.
To hide the wicked plan our hearts both know.

Act 2, Scene 1

[An open courtyard in Macbeth's castle a few hours after the feast. Enter Banquo and his son, Fleance, who is carrying a light]

Banquo: What's the time, boy?

Fleance: I did not hear the clock. It's very dark. There is no moon tonight.

Banquo: The stars are covered. There are no lights in Heaven. The night is dark, black, like my thoughts.
My heart is heavy and I cannot sleep.
Who's there?

[Enter Macbeth, with a servant]

Macbeth: A friend.

Banquo: Can't you sleep either? The King's in bed.
He is well pleased with you and sends you gifts.
He has given me this diamond for your wife,
His gracious hostess, who has pleased him too.

Macbeth: We did our best. We did not have enough time to prepare.

Banquo: But all went well.
I dreamt last night of the all-seeing sisters.
Their words to you were partly true.

Macbeth: I haven't thought about them.
But what they said about my being King was strange.
Ideas like that are dangerous. They could be treason.

Banquo: We need to talk about them.

Macbeth: We are the King's friends, not his enemies.

Banquo: Of course. It is not wrong to talk about the witches.
It may be wrong to trust them. Good night.

Macbeth: Good night, sleep well.

Banquo: Thanks, sir. May you sleep well too.

[Exit Banquo and Fleance]

Macbeth: *[To his servant]*
Say to my wife, that when my drink is ready,

To ring the bell. Then go to bed.
[As Macbeth is waiting, he imagines a dagger in the air in front of him]
Is this a dagger I can see before me, its handle near my hand?
Let me take hold of it – no, it's gone, it's air.
It was unreal, a picture in my mind.
But, see, it's there again, to lead me on.
And now fresh blood is dripping from it …
No, there's nothing there.
It is my murderous mind and nothing more
That makes me see the dagger.
Now half the world's asleep and in the darkness,
Murder and mischief[53] rule. Wolves howl.
Night is the time for witchcraft and for evil.
Now when I move, I must be silent.
The stones on which I walk must not betray[54] me
And stop me carrying out my wicked plan.
[The bell rings]
The bell calls me to murder. If I go, it's done.
Do not hear it, Duncan – that same bell
Is calling you to Heaven, or to Hell.

Macbeth: *Now o'er the one half-world*
Nature seems dead, and wicked dreams abuse
The curtain'd sleep; witchcraft celebrates
Pale Hecat's offerings: and wither'd murder
Alarum'd by his sentinel, the wolf,
Whose howl's his watch, thus with his stealthy pace,
With Tarquin's ravishing strides, towards his design
Moves like a ghost. Thou sure and firm-set Earth,
Hear not my steps, which way they walk, for fear
Thy very stones prate of my whereabout,
And take the present horror from the time,
Which now suits with it. Whiles I threat, he lives:

Words to the heat of deeds too cold breath gives.
[A bell rings] I go, and it is done: the bell invites me.
Hear it not, Duncan, for it is a knell
That summons thee to Heaven, or to Hell.

o'er = over
Hecat = a goddess of the underworld
alarum'd = sounded an alarm
sentinel = a guard
stealthy = quiet and secretive
thou = you
thy = your
very (stones) = the stones themselves
prate = talk about
whereabout = where I am
suits = agrees
knell = sound of a bell
summons = calls

Act 2, Scene 2

[Inside Macbeth's castle. Exit Macbeth towards Duncan's bedroom. Then Lady Macbeth enters, a cup of wine in her hand. She smiles]

Lady Macbeth: The wine that made them drunk, has made me bold.

It drowned their fire, but it has strengthened mine.

Listen!

No, it's nothing but the owl, the bird of night.

Macbeth's at work.

I drugged the servants' drink. I'm sure they will not wake.

Macbeth: *[offstage]*

Who calls? Who's there?

Lady Macbeth: Oh, no! They've woken up. The deed's not done.

But the attempt betrays us!

Listen! What's that noise?

I left the daggers near. He must have seen them.

If the King had not looked like my father as he slept,

I would have murdered him myself.

[Enter Macbeth with the blood-covered daggers]

My husband!

Macbeth: I have done the deed. Did you not hear a noise?

Lady Macbeth: I heard the owl cry. Did you not speak?

Macbeth: When?

Lady Macbeth: Just now.

Macbeth: As I came down the stairs?

Lady Macbeth: That's right.

Macbeth: Listen!

Who's sleeping in the second room?

Lady Macbeth: The King's young son, Donalbain.

[Macbeth holds out his hands and the blood-covered daggers]

Macbeth: This is a fearful sight.

Lady Macbeth: A foolish thought to say a fearful sight.

Macbeth: One laughed in his sleep and one cried 'Murder!'
As though he saw my bloody hands.
They both woke up, then they began to pray.
One said 'God bless us'. The other said 'Amen'.
I wanted to say Amen too, but I couldn't.
Lady Macbeth: Don't think about that now.
Macbeth: You do not understand. I couldn't say it.
Lady Macbeth: Don't talk like that – you'll send us mad.
Macbeth: I thought I heard a voice cry, 'Sleep no more!
Macbeth has murdered sleep.'
That sweet sleep that calms our troubled thoughts.
Sleep that brings rest to tired minds and bodies
Sleep that's both medicine and food …
Lady Macbeth: What do you mean?
Macbeth: And still that voice cried, 'Sleep no more!
Glamis has murdered sleep, and so Cawdor
Shall sleep no more. Macbeth shall sleep no more.'
Lady Macbeth: Quiet. Talk like that will send us mad.
Now get some water, clean this blood away.
[She sees the daggers]
Why did you bring these daggers from the room?
Carry them back and coat the men with blood.
Macbeth: I won't go back. I dare not think what I have done.
I cannot look at him again.
Lady Macbeth: Weak-minded coward! Give me the daggers.
Asleep or dead? What is the difference?
Children are afraid of death, not soldiers.
I'll cover those two men with Duncan's blood
Then all will know they're guilty.
[Exit Lady Macbeth. There is loud knocking at the castle gate]
Macbeth: Who's knocking at the gate? I cannot bear it.
My hands are red. I dare not look at them.
Will all the water of the world's great oceans
Wash this blood from my hands?

36

Why did you bring these daggers from the room?
Carry them back and coat the men with blood.

No, never! One drop of Duncan's blood
Will turn the green sea red.

Macbeth: *Whence is that knocking?*
How is't with me, when every noise appals me?
What hands are here? Ha! They pluck out mine eyes!
Will all great Neptune's ocean wash this blood
Clean from my hand? No; this my hand will rather
The multitudinous seas incarnadine,
Making the green one red.

appals = horrifies
pluck = pull
Neptune = god of the sea
multitudinous = of many parts
incarnadine = colour something red

[Enter Lady Macbeth]
Lady Macbeth: Look, now my hands are red, like yours.
But I'm not white with fear, like you.
Someone's at the gate. Let's go back to our room.
A little water will soon clean our hands – that's easy.
[Loud knocking]
More knocking! Your courage left you for a time.
Put on your night-gown. Everyone must think
We were both in bed. Come on, the deed is done.
Macbeth: I still cannot believe what I have done.
I dare not think about it.
[Loud knocking]
More knocking!
Oh, wake Duncan up … how I wish you could!

Act 2, Scene 3

[The knocking at Macbeth's castle gate goes on. After some time, an old porter opens the gate and lets in Macduff and Lennox]

Macduff: You got up late. Did you go to bed late too?

Porter: There was a big feast, sir, in honour of the King. Lots Of good food, sir. Drink too.

Macduff: I can see you had plenty of that. Is your master up yet?

[Exit porter. Enter Macbeth, in his dressing gown]

Ah, here he is now.

Lennox: Good morning, noble sir.

Macbeth: Good morning to both of you.

Macduff: Is the King awake yet, worthy thane?

Macbeth: Not yet.

Macduff: The King told me to come and see him early. I hope that I am not late.

Macbeth: I'll take you to him. Follow me. There is the door.

Macduff: I'll go inside and wake him.

[Exit Macduff]

Lennox: Does the King plan to leave today?

Macbeth: He does. That's what he said last night.

Lennox: I hope he slept well. The wind was very strong. It blew down trees and damaged all our houses. Strange cries were heard and dreadful dying screams. The owl sang all night long to warn us all, And some men said they felt the earth shake too.

Macbeth: Yes, it was a rough night.

[Enter Macduff]

Macduff: Oh, horror, horror, horror! I cannot speak. I don't know what to say!

Macbeth:
Lennox: } What's the matter?

Macduff: The most awful thing has happened!

He, whom God had chosen, has been taken.
I mean his sacred[55] life's been taken, stolen
From him by foul murder!
Macbeth: Life taken? Murder? Is someone dead?
Lennox: Do you mean the King?
Macduff: See for yourselves. The sight will strike you blind.
I cannot speak of it. It is too horrible.
[Exit Macbeth and Lennox]
Awake! Awake! Wake up everyone!
Ring the alarm bell. Murder! Treason!
Banquo and Donalbain! Malcolm, wake up!
Wake up and see this horror, if you dare!
[The alarm bell rings. Enter Lady Macbeth]
Lady Macbeth: What has happened?
What is the cause of all this dreadful noise
That wakes the peaceful sleepers in this house?
Speak, speak!
Macduff: Oh, gracious lady,
It's not right for you to hear the fearful news.
Heard by a woman's ear, the word would kill again.
[Enter Banquo, half-dressed]
Oh, Banquo, Banquo! Our royal master's murdered.
Lady Macbeth: No! How terrible!
Murdered in our house?
Banquo: Murder is cruel, anywhere.
Macduff, I pray you, say it is not true.
[Enter Macbeth and Lennox]
Macbeth: If I had died an hour before this time,
I would have died happy. But from this moment,
There's nothing left worth living for.
Nothing has meaning, now that honour's dead.
All that we live for, has been taken away.
[Enter Malcolm and Donalbain]
Donalbain: What is the problem here?

Macbeth: The problem's yours, but you don't know it.
The noble King who gave you both your lives
Has left us.
Macduff: Your royal father's murdered.
Malcolm: Oh! By whom?
Lennox: The servants sleeping in his room have done it –
That's what we think.
Their hands and faces were all red with blood.
So were their daggers. They stared at us, half-mad.
No man is safe with them.
Macbeth: I thought so too and, in sudden anger,
I killed them both.
Macduff: Why? We should have questioned them.
Macbeth: Who can be wise, surprised, calm and angry,
Loyal and neutral, all in a moment?
No one. Strong feelings made me act.
I did not stop to think. There lay Duncan,
His silver skin covered with gold-red blood
And every wound was like a door,
Through which death had entered.
There lay the murderers, red with Duncan's blood.
There lay their daggers, blood-red too.
Who could hold back from killing them?
No one with a loving heart and courage
To prove that love!

Macbeth: *Who can be wise, amaz'd, temperate and furious,*
Loyal and neutral, in a moment? No man:
Th'expedition of my violent love
Outran the pauser, reason. Here lay Duncan,
His silver skin lac'd with his golden blood;
And his gash'd stabs look'd like a breach in nature
For ruin's wasteful entrance: there, the murderers,
Steep'd in the colours of their trade, their daggers

41

Unmannerly breech'd with gore: who could refrain,
That had a heart to love, and in that heart
Courage to make love known?

expedition = speed
pauser = makes you hesitate
lac'd = decorated
breach = a hole made in a wall (in war)
steep'd = soaked
unmannerly = indecently
breech'd = clothed
gore = blood

Lady Macbeth: Help me! I am ill.
Macduff: Someone help the lady! She has fainted.
[Enter servants]
Malcolm: *[To his brother]*
Why do we stand here silent? We should be the first to speak.
Donalbain: What can we say? We may be the next to die.
Let's go, before our tears begin to fall.
Malcolm: It is too soon for us to take revenge.
Banquo: *[To Lady Macbeth's servants]* Help the lady.
[The servants take her out]
And when we have had time to dress ourselves,
Let's meet again, discuss this dreadful deed
And then decide on action.
Fears and terrors fill my mind, but I stand here
Under God's protection. When I know the truth,
I'll fight against this treason.
Macduff: And so will I.
Macbeth: When we are ready, we'll meet in the hall, together.
All: We agree.
[All exit except Malcolm and Donalbain]
Malcolm: What will you do? We're not safe here.
Trust no one. I shall go to England.
Donalbain: And I shall go to Ireland.

Someone help the lady! She has fainted.

We shall be safer if we are not together.
If we stay here, we'll be the next to die.
Malcolm: Our father's killer may still be alive
Let's go before he kills again.
We'll ride away, without a word to anyone.
Donalbain: There's nothing for us here. We'll go at once.
[Exit Malcolm and Donalbain]

Act 2, Scene 4

[Ross meets Macduff, as he is leaving Macbeth's castle]
Ross: What news, good Macduff?
Is it known yet who did the bloody deed?
Macduff: The two killed by Macbeth. That's what men say.
Ross: Then curse[56] them both.
What did they hope to gain from it?
Macduff: They were paid to do it. Or so it's thought.
Malcolm and Donalbain, the King's own sons,
Have run away – left Scotland. So people think
Those young men planned the murder.
Ross: That's an unnatural deed.
Ambition makes no sense when evil sons
Kill their own father.
Then, I suppose, Macbeth will wear the crown.
Macduff: Yes, Macbeth will be our King. He has already gone
To royal Scone, for his coronation[57].
Ross: Where is Duncan's body?
Macduff: It has been taken to the royal place, where Scotland's
kings are buried.
Ross: Will you go to Scone?
Macduff: No, my good friend. I'm going home, to Fife.
Ross: Well, I'll go to Scone, to see the coronation.
Macduff: Let's hope our new King's worthy of his crown.
Farewell, good thane.
Ross: Go safely, good Macduff.

Act 3, Scene 1

[Inside the royal palace at Forres. Several weeks have passed. Macbeth is now King of Scotland and Lady Macbeth is his Queen. A great feast has been planned for that night at the palace. All the thanes have been invited. Enter Banquo, who is speaking his thoughts aloud]

Banquo: You have it all now – King, Cawdor, Glamis –
As those all-seeing sisters promised and I fear
You acted wickedly to get the crown.
They said no child of yours would be a king,
That I myself would start a royal line
And be the father of so many kings.
 If the witches spoke the truth about my future
As they have of yours, Macbeth, then I have hope
Of greatness still to come.
I must not speak of that – I'll keep it to myself.

[A trumpet sounds. Enter Macbeth and Lady Macbeth, wearing their royal crowns, attended by servants]

Macbeth: Here's our most honoured guest.

Lady Macbeth: If we forget our noble Banquo,
Our feast will have no meaning.

Macbeth: Tonight we plan a royal supper, sir.
I'd like you to be there.

Banquo: It is my loyal duty, sir. I'm happy to obey.

Macbeth: Do you plan to ride this afternoon?

Banquo: Yes, my good lord.

Macbeth: We would have welcomed all your good advice
At today's meeting. Never mind,
I'll talk with you tomorrow. Are you going far?

Banquo: As far, my lord, as will fill up the time
Between now and supper.
It may be dark when I return.

Macbeth: Be sure you do not miss our feast.

Banquo: My lord, I will not.

Macbeth: We hear the evil sons of Duncan live in
England now and Ireland, not admitting
Their father's cruel murder, but telling everyone
A strangely different story.
We'll talk of that tomorrow – and of another matter
Important to us both. So farewell now,
Until your return tonight.
Does your son, Fleance, ride with you?
Banquo: Yes, my good lord, he does.
Macbeth: Then ride safely, both of you.
Enjoy yourselves.
Everyone is free to stay or go, till seven tonight.
I'll spend the time alone. God bless you all!
[Exit all except Macbeth and a servant]
Are those men I sent for here?
Servant: They are, my lord, outside the palace gate.
Macbeth: Bring them to me.
[Exit servant]
[To himself] All my power is nothing if I'm not safe.
Banquo's my problem now. He's an honest man
And so I fear him. He's afraid of nothing.
He always thinks before he acts. He's dangerous.
When the all-seeing sisters called me King,
He asked them questions too.
Then the all-seeing ones foretold our futures
And mine was black, indeed. Yes, I'd be King,
But after me, no son of mine would rule.
Banquo would be father to a line of kings –
King after king … I wear the crown, it's true,
But any royal power I have will die with me.
I have committed murder, but for Banquo's children.
My peace has gone for ever, just for them.
When I am dead, my soul will go to Hell –
And all for his children, to make his children kings!

47

That must not happen. My fate is in my hands
And I shall win! Who's there?

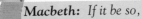

Macbeth: *If it be so,*
For Banquo's issue have I fil'd my mind,
For them the gracious Duncan I have murder'd,
Put rancours in the vessel of my peace,
Only for them; and mine eternal jewel
Given to the common enemy of man,
To make them kings, the seed of Banquo kings!
Rather than so, come Fate into the list,
And champion me to th'utterance. Who's there?

issue = descendants
fil'd = ruined
rancours = poison, evil thoughts
vessel = cup
eternal jewel = my immortal soul
seed = descendants
list = place where knights fight
champion = challenge
utterance = death

[Enter servant with two murderers. Macbeth to servant]
Go to the door. Wait there until I call.
[To murderers] We spoke together yesterday, didn't we?
1ˢᵗ Murderer: We did, my lord.
Macbeth: Then you must both remember what I said.
For many years, you thought I was your enemy.
But now you know the truth.
Banquo is the evil man you ought to hate.
He is the enemy who has destroyed your lives.
1ˢᵗ Murderer: That's what you told us and we both believe you.
Macbeth: Then, why have you done nothing?
Have you forgotten how this man has harmed you?
Are you dogs or men?

Murderers: We are men, my lord.

Macbeth: Then if you're men, you must want revenge
And now's your chance to get it.
I want Banquo dead and so do you.
Kill him today. You'll have my thanks
And my protection. What do you say?

1st Murderer: I've nothing left to lose – I'll do it.

2nd Murderer: And so will I.

Macbeth: Remember, Banquo is your enemy and he's mine.

Murderers: True, my good lord.

Macbeth: Like you, I want him dead. But it must be in secret.
I am the King. I could kill Banquo.
But that would not be wise.
Banquo has his friends – they are my friends too,
I do not wish to lose them. So I ask your help.
You will be satisfied – rewarded too by me.
Do you agree to do it?

2nd Murderer: We shall, my lord, do anything you ask.

1st Murderer: My life for his ...

Macbeth: It must be done tonight, some distance
from the palace.
His son Fleance will be with him. He must die too.
Nothing must go wrong. You understand me?

Murderers: We do, my lord.

Macbeth: Go now. Keep out of sight. I'll see you later.

[Exit murderers]

That's settled, then. Banquo, your soul's flight
If it finds Heaven, finds it out tonight.

[Exit Macbeth]

Act 3, Scene 2

[Enter Lady Macbeth, speaking aloud to herself]
Lady Macbeth: The servant said my lord was here.
I need to speak to him and learn his thoughts ...
What we now have, brings no delight.
Our brightest day has turned to darkest night.
We are not safe, there is no joy,
When guilt and horror our own lives destroy.
[Enter Macbeth]
Why, my dear lord, do you walk alone,
With only your sad thoughts for company?
Such thoughts should all be buried with the dead.
Nothing can change things now. What's done is done.
Macbeth: The deed's half done. The snake is wounded,
But we have not killed it. It will turn again
And poison us – there's nothing we can do.
I eat in fear, my dreams are terrible.
I'd rather end it all, than live like this –
Tormented[58] day and night by thoughts and dreams.
Duncan is in his grave[59], where he sleeps well.
No treason, fear or harm can touch him there.
Lady Macbeth: Come, my dear lord, put all these fears aside.
Be bright and cheerful among your guests tonight.
Macbeth: Of course, I will, my love, and so will you.
Pay most attention, dear, to noble Banquo.
Your looks and words must flatter him
To keep us safe. I'll do the same.
Our faces are the masks that hide black hearts –
Black with our evil thoughts.
Lady Macbeth: Don't talk like that.
Macbeth: Oh, dreadful thoughts torment me, my dear wife.
Banquo and his Fleance are alive, you know ...
Lady Macbeth: They will not live for ever. I know that too.

Macbeth: That's true. That's very true. Be happy then.
Before the last light of bright day has gone
And been replaced by blackness, there shall be done
A truly wicked deed.
Lady Macbeth: What deed? What will be done?
Macbeth: It's better you don't know. Approve it, when it's done.
Come, black night, and with your darkness
Blind the bright eye of day.
So that the murderer can end the life
Of him who walled me up in fear.
Look where darkness comes, as birds fly to their nests.
Good things of day will soon all be asleep
As night's cruel hunters wake to take their place.
My words are strange, I know, but do not fear.
Evil grows darker still, when night is here.
Each wicked deed strengthens the next to come.
So, dear wife, go with me.
[Exit Macbeth and Lady Macbeth]

Act 3, Scene 3

[A short distance from the palace. Enter two murderers]

1st Murderer: The last light of day is going in the west
Now Banquo must be near and riding fast.

2nd Murderer: Listen! I hear horses.

1st Murderer: It's Banquo then, and Fleance.
Now they've stopped.

Banquo: *[Offstage, to his servants]*
Ho! Give me a light there. Take the horses.

2nd Murderer: That's Banquo's voice.
The last part of the journey's made on foot
Along this narrow path.

[Enter Banquo and Fleance, with a light]

1st Murderer: Look! A light, a light! It's them!

2nd Murderer: Quiet! Wait until they pass us.

Banquo: *[To Fleance]* I think that it will rain tonight.

1st Murderer: Let it come down!

[The murderers stab Banquo, who falls down]

Banquo: Oh, traitors! Run, good Fleance, run!
Revenge! Revenge!

[Banquo dies and Fleance runs away]

2nd Murderer: Who put out the light?

1st Murderer: Banquo is killed, but his son's escaped.

2nd Murderer: Then our job is not complete.

1st Murderer: We'll leave the body here
And tell Macbeth what's done, what's left undone.

[Exit murderers]

Let it come down!

Act 3, Scene 4

[The great hall of the palace. There are two thrones at the main table for Macbeth and Lady Macbeth. Other long tables are for their guests. Enter Macbeth and Lady Macbeth, wearing their crowns. Their guests follow them]

Macbeth: You know your places, please sit down
To one and all, a cheerful welcome.

Guests: Thanks to your majesty.

[Macbeth leads Lady Macbeth to her throne]

Macbeth: I'll walk about the hall, speak to our guests.
Our gracious hostess sits on her royal throne
From where she'll give her welcome.

Lady Macbeth: I do it now, my lord, to all our friends.
And from my heart, I truly welcome them.

[All stand and bow to Lady Macbeth]

Macbeth: See how our guests return your thanks.
Here is an empty chair – I shall sit there.
Enjoy yourselves and then we'll drink a toast[60].

[Enter 1st murderer. Macbeth goes to speak to him]

There's blood upon your face.

1st Murderer: It's Banquo's then.

Macbeth: I'd rather see you here than Banquo. Is he dead?

1st Murderer: My lord, his throat is cut – I did it.

Macbeth: Then you are the best of all cut-throats.
Yet he's as good, who cut the throat of Fleance.
If you did that too, you have no equal.

1st Murderer: My royal lord, Fleance escaped.

Macbeth: Then all my fears return. Fleance's death
Would have made me safe. Now I'm trapped again,
Imprisoned by my fears. But Banquo's dead?

1st Murderer: Yes, my good lord. Dead in a ditch[61], he lies.
With more than twenty cuts upon his head.
Each cut enough to kill him.

Macbeth: My thanks for that. The snake is dead.
The son who's harmless now, will poison when he's grown.
Revenge will follow later.
Go now. I'll speak to you again tomorrow.
[Exit murderer]
Lady Macbeth: *[To Macbeth]* My royal lord, why do you forget
your guests?
The feast is ruined when the host's not there.
You must drink with them, give the toasts
That join them to you, make them yours.
If not, they'd better eat at home.
[The Ghost of Banquo enters and sits on the empty chair]
Macbeth: What you say is true, dear wife.
[To the guests] Noble thanes,
Eat and drink well.
Here's to your good health!
[Macbeth drinks]
Lennox: My noble lord, sit down with us.
Macbeth: If Banquo, my dear friend, was with us now,
All the great men of Scotland would be honoured.
I'd rather blame good Banquo for his absence[62],
Than fear he's come to harm.
Ross: He was wrong to break his promise.
Please sit, my lord.
Macbeth: The table's full.
Lennox: Here's a place for you, sir.
Macbeth: Where?
Lennox: Here, my good lord. Why, what's the matter?
[Macbeth has seen the Ghost of Banquo]
Macbeth: Who has done this?
Lennox: What, my good lord?
Macbeth: *[To the Ghost of Banquo]*
You cannot say I did it! Do not shake
Your bloody head at me!

Ross: Gentlemen, stand up. Our royal host's not well.
Lady Macbeth: *[Calmly]* Sit, my good friends, he's often ill like this.
He'll soon be well again, you must believe me.
If you notice him, you'll make him worse.
Please sit and eat.
[To Macbeth] Are you a man?
Macbeth: Yes, and a brave one, who's seen such dreadful sights
Devils would fear to see.
Lady Macbeth: This is all nonsense.
Your fearful mind leads you to see strange things –
Like that imagined dagger, which, you said,
Showed you the way to Duncan. Your fear
Of things not seen is shameful.
Why all those looks of horror at an empty chair?
Macbeth: I beg you, look at it! Look! Can't you see it?
[To the Ghost of Banquo] What do I care? If you can nod, speak too.
If graves give back the dead, like this,
Let birds of prey tear their cold bodies up.
[The Ghost of Banquo disappears]
Lady Macbeth: Have you gone mad?
Macbeth: As sure as I stand here, I saw him.
Lady Macbeth: Shame on you, shame.
Macbeth: Blood has been spilt before. In days gone by,
Before countries had their laws to keep them safe,
Yes – and since then, murders have been committed,
Too terrible to speak about. It used to be
That when a man received a fatal cut, he'd die,
And that would be the end. But now men rise again
Though they have suffered twenty such blows –
And push us from our chairs. This is more strange
Than any murder is.

I beg you, look at it! Look! Can't you see it?

Macbeth: *Blood hath been shed ere now, in th'olden time,*
Ere humane statute purg'd the gentle weal;
Aye, and since too, murders have been perform'd
Too terrible for the ear: the time has been,
That, when the brains were out, the man would die,
And there an end: but now they rise again,
With twenty mortal murders on their crowns,
And push us from our stools. This is more strange
Than such a murder is.

ere = before
shed = spilt, lost
statute = law
purg'd = cleansed
weal = society
aye = yes
mortal = causing death

Lady Macbeth: My royal lord, you must think of your guests.
Macbeth: I had forgotten them …
[To the guests] Do not be surprised, my noble friends.
I have a strange illness, but it is nothing
To those who know me. So love and health to all!
I'll drink another toast! Then I'll sit down.
[The Ghost enters again and sits down on the empty chair]
So now I drink a toast to all our guests
And to our dear friend, Banquo, whom we miss.
I wish that he were here.
A toast to him and all of you! A toast to all!
[Macbeth drinks]
Guests: A toast to all! Our duty is to you, sir!
[Macbeth turns and sees the Ghost]
Macbeth: Out of my sight! Away, away!
Let the earth cover you!
Your bones are lifeless and your blood is cold.
Those eyes you stare with can see nothing now.

Lady Macbeth: Think nothing of this, my good lords!
The illness will soon pass. Please, enjoy the feast.
Macbeth: *[To the Ghost]*
What any brave man dares, I would dare too.
Take any other fearful shape and I will fight you.
I'll fight the wildest animal and feel no fear.
But this strange, dreadful sight I cannot face.
If you were alive again, your sword in hand
I'd fight you bravely and not feel afraid.
Oh, go, go, you awful Ghost!
Unreal shadow, go! Leave me alone.
[Exit the Ghost]
Why, now it's gone, I am a man again.
Sit down, good friends, sit down.
Lady Macbeth: *[Impatiently to Macbeth]* It's too late now,
Our feast is ruined.
Our guests are all afraid of your strange words.
Macbeth: Can such sights be true?
Can pictures from my mind so frighten me?
I do not understand. You must have seen this sight
But yet you feel no fear.
Ross: What sight, my lord?
Lady Macbeth: *[Fearfully]* Please do not speak to him.
Your questions anger him.
Good night to all. Please leave as quickly as you can.
Go, please go at once.
Lennox: Good night. I hope the King will soon be well again.
Lady Macbeth: Good night to all.
[Exit all the guests]
Macbeth: When there is murder, blood always finds revenge.
Through many signs the deed will be revealed[63].
Stones, so men say, will move and trees may speak.
The cries of owls and ravens, if well understood,
Will tell the world the murderer's guilty secret.

Is the night ended yet?

Lady Macbeth: The morning's almost here.

Macbeth: Why did Macduff refuse to come tonight?

Lady Macbeth: Did he refuse? Are you really sure?

Macbeth: I was told so. I will soon find out.
I have paid spies in everybody's house …
Early tomorrow – I won't waste any time,
I'll go again to the all-seeing sisters.
They must know more and I must know it too,
However bad the news. All other problems
Must be put aside until I know the truth.
I feel I'm walking through a stream of blood,
Both wide and deep. I'm in so far that going back
Would be as difficult as going on. I have strange thoughts
That must be changed to deeds.
There's no time left to think about them first.

Lady Macbeth: You need to sleep, to calm your mind.

Macbeth: Come then, let us sleep. The fearful sights I see,
Show I'm a child in deeds of treachery[64].
I'll learn by practising more wicked deeds
As I grow stronger still in evil.

[Exit Macbeth and Lady Macbeth]

Act 3, Scene 5

[A castle in Scotland. Enter Lennox and Ross. They are talking about Macbeth]

Lennox: I agree with all you've said. It's very strange.
There are many questions now that need an answer.
Our noble Duncan was Macbeth's honoured guest.
Duncan died … Banquo and his son went out too late …
Banquo died too. His son Fleance ran away – so
The son must have killed the father!
In the same way Prince Malcolm and his brother
Killed the King, their father, and they fled[65] too!

Ross: Then how unhappy Macbeth was!
How wise he was to kill the drunken servants,
Before they could deny their part in murder.

Lennox: Those living sons must not come near Macbeth.
I fear he'd do them harm. The good Macduff
Has kept away from Macbeth too. That's angered him.

Ross: Sir, can you say where brave Macduff has gone?

Lennox: He's on his way to England, where Prince Malcolm
Lives in the English court.
Together they will ask King Edward for an army
To march against the tyrant. With Macbeth dead,
We may sleep at night, keep ourselves safe
And live as honest men again.

Ross: Does Macbeth know where Macduff is?

Lennox: Yes. Macduff was ordered home, but he won't come.
So now Macbeth prepares for war.

Ross: Then let us pray the English army marches soon.

Lennox: I pray for victory and the tyrant's death.

Ross: And peace for our sad country too. Farewell, sir.

Lennox: Farewell, noble thane.

Act 4, Scene 1

[It is midnight. In a dark cave, the three witches are standing around a cauldron[66] hanging over a fire. They are making a spell. Thunder can be heard and the cries of animals]

1st Witch: Round and round our cauldron go
In the magic mixture throw.
Poison from a toad[67] I've got
Throw that first into the pot.
All Witches: Double, double, double trouble,
Fire burn and cauldron bubble.
2nd Witch: Here's a slice of slimy[68] snake
In the cauldron boil and bake.
Eye of fly and toe of frog
Claw of bat and ear of dog.
Snake's poisoned tongue and cruel wasp's sting,
Lizard's leg and young owl's wing.
For a spell of powerful trouble
This soup from Hell must boil and bubble.
All Witches: As we make you double trouble,
Fire burn and cauldron bubble.
3rd Witch: Skin of dragon, wolf's sharp claw,
Bone from a dead witch's jaw[69],
Stomach of man-eating shark
Poisoned plants, picked in the dark.
Mix the soup and stir it well
To make the magic of our spell.
All Witches: We will double all your trouble,
Fire burn and cauldron bubble.
2nd Witch: Cool it with some monkey's blood
Then the spell is firm and good.
[She listens] By the pricking[70] of my thumbs
Something wicked this way comes!
Open locks, whoever knocks!

[Enter Macbeth]
Macbeth: At last I've found you, black and midnight witches!
What mischief are you doing now?
All Witches: Something too bad to tell.
Macbeth: By all the evil powers that you possess
I must be told the answer that I seek[71].
Though you can raise strong winds that will destroy
The greatest buildings on the earth,
Though you can make great waves and sink our ships,
Destroy our crops[72], destroy the earth itself,
I must be answered.
1st Witch: Speak!
2nd Witch: Ask us!
3rd Witch: We'll answer.
1st Witch: Say if you would rather hear it from our mouths
Or from our masters'.
Macbeth: Call your masters! Let me see them!
1st Witch: Pour pig's blood in the boiling pot.
Sweat from a hanging man I've got.
All Witches: Come high, come low
Your powerful magic you must show!
[Thunder. The first spirit is a head wearing a soldier's helmet, looking like Macbeth himself. It rises up from the cauldron]
Macbeth: Tell me, you unknown power …
1st Witch: Our master knows your thoughts.
Hear him, but say nothing.
1st Spirit: Macbeth, Macbeth, Macbeth! Beware Macduff!
Beware the Thane of Fife! Let me go, I've said enough.
[Spirit goes back into the cauldron]
Macbeth: Whoever you may be, I thank you for your warning.
You have told me my own fears. But one word more …
1st Witch: You cannot tell him what to say.
Here's another spirit, more powerful than the first.
[Thunder. The spirit of a blood-covered child rises from the cauldron]

Macbeth, Macbeth, Macbeth! Beware Macduff!
Beware the Thane of Fife!

2ⁿᵈ Spirit: Be cruel, bold and strong. Fear not the power of man.
No man of woman born shall harm Macbeth.
[Spirit goes back into the cauldron]
Macbeth: Then live, Macduff. I have no fear of you.
But I'll make sure this promise does come true
And free myself from fate. You will not live, Macduff.
I'll laugh at fear and be afraid of nothing.
[Thunder. The third is a crowned child, holding a tree spirit]
What is this? A child who will be King?
All Witches: Listen, but do not speak.
3ʳᵈ Spirit: Be proud, brave as a lion and have no fear
Of any enemy, away or near.
Macbeth shall never be defeated till
Great Birnam Wood to high Dunsinane Hill
Shall move against him.
[Spirit goes back into the cauldron]
Macbeth: That will never be.
Who can make forests move or tell a tree
To pull up its deep roots? This is good news.
Come not again to haunt⁷³ me, Ghost of Banquo.
Unless the forests move. So Macbeth
Will keep his throne and live his life unharmed.
Yet I must still know one more thing …
Will anyone from Banquo's family reign in Scotland?

Macbeth: *That will never be:*
Who can impress the forest, bid the tree
Unfix his earth-bound root? Sweet bodement good.
Rebellious dead, rise never, till the wood
Of Birnam rise, and our high-plac'd Macbeth
Shall live the lease of Nature, pay his breath
To time, and mortal custom. Yet my heart
Throbs to know one more thing: tell me (if your art

Can tell so much): shall Banquo's issue ever
Reign in this kingdom?

impress = force to join an army
bid = order
bodement = sign, forecast
rebellious = behaving unnaturally
rise = come to life
lease of Nature = normal length of life
throbs = beats fast

All Witches: Do not ask to know more.

Macbeth: I will be answered! If I don't learn this,

An everlasting curse will fall on you. Tell me!

[Strange music is heard. The witches' cauldron disappears into the ground]

What is that noise? What is happening now?

1ˢᵗ Witch: Show!

2ⁿᵈ Witch: Show!

3ʳᵈ Witch: Show!

All Witches: Show his eyes and grieve[74] his heart.

Come like shadows, then depart.

[A line of eight kings appears at the back of the cave. The last king carries a mirror, which shows even more kings. The Ghost of Banquo follows them]

Macbeth: You look too much like Banquo and your golden crown

Glitters so brightly that it burns my eyes!

And here's a second one, crowned like the first.

And then a third, the same! You wicked witches!

Why do you show me this? A fourth! No, no!

Does Banquo's line stretch to the end of time?

Yet another! A seventh? I'll see no more!

And yet the line goes on. Here's the eighth

And in his mirror more and more appear

And so the line goes on. Oh dreadful sight!
So now I see it's true – blood-covered Banquo
Smiles at me and shows me they are his!
[More strange music. The witches laugh, dance together and then disappear into the foggy air]
Macbeth: Where are they? Gone!
This day and hour will now be cursed for ever.
[Macbeth calls to Lennox]
Where are you? Come here now!
[Enter Lennox]
Lennox: What do you want, my lord?
Macbeth: Did you see the three sisters?
Lennox: No, my good lord.
Macbeth: Surely they passed by you?
Lennox: No, they did not, my lord.
Macbeth: Cursed be the air that carried them away.
And damned[75] are those who put their trust in them.
I heard the sound of horses. Who was it?
Lennox: Some messengers, my lord. Macduff has fled to England.
Macbeth: *[To himself]* To England? Then I have no time
And from this moment, deeds must follow thoughts.
I will attack the castle of Macduff.
His wife, his children, family and friends – they all must die.
But no more dreadful sights!
[To Lennox] Where are those messengers? Take me to them now.
[Exit Macbeth and Lennox]

Act 4, Scene 2

[Macduff's castle, in Fife. Enter Lady Macduff, a boy (Lady Macduff's son) and Ross]

Lady Macduff: Why has my husband gone and left us here, alone?

Ross: You must be patient, madam.

Lady Macduff: *[Angrily]* Patient? *He* was not. Macduff is not a traitor.
But leaving us has made him look like one.

Ross: He must have had good reason.

Lady Macduff: Good reason? To leave his wife? His children?
To leave his castle? Everything he owns?
He does not love us. Even birds protect their young.
My husband is a coward and a fool.
No. His leaving is against all reason.

Ross: My dearest madam, please do calm yourself.
I know Macduff is good – wise, brave and well-informed.
I dare not tell you more.
Scotland is now full of fears and lies. Men are afraid,
But don't know what they fear. Now I must go.
[Turns to speak to Lady Macduff's son]
I'll soon be here again. Let's hope that things get better.
Farewell, dear child, and may God protect you.

Lady Macduff: He had a father, but that father's gone.

Ross: If I stay longer, we all shall be in trouble. Farewell.
[Exit Ross]

Lady Macduff: *[To her son]* So, my son, your father's dead. How will you live now?

Boy: As birds do, Mother.

Lady Macduff: What do you mean? By eating worms?

Boy: I'll pick up what I can, as they do, Mother.

Lady Macduff: Poor bird! You must not be afraid. You won't be caught.

Boy: That's true. No one tries to catch a *little* bird.
My father is not dead, although you say so.
Lady Macduff: Yes, he is dead. How will you get on without a
father?
Boy: And how will you get on without a husband?
Lady Macduff: Oh, I shall find another, soon enough.
Boy: Was my father a traitor, Mother?
Lady Macduff: Yes, he was.
Boy: What is a traitor?
Lady Macduff: Well, someone who swears, and lies.
Boy: And are they all traitors … the people who do that?
Lady Macduff: Yes, they are, and they must be hanged.
Boy: Who must hang them?
Lady Macduff: Well, the honest men.
Boy: Then the liars and swearers are fools, for there
Are enough of them to attack and hang the honest men.
Lady Macduff: Now God help you, poor youngster.
But how will you get on without a father?
Boy: If he was dead, you'd cry for him.
As you don't cry, it's a good sign – that I'll soon have a new
father!
Lady Macduff: Poor little boy! How cleverly you talk!
[Enter messenger]
Messenger: God bless you, madam! I know who you are,
Although you don't know me.
Take my advice, there is much danger here.
This castle is not safe, so leave at once.
I am frightening you, but I must do it.
Go, with your children, and Heaven help you all!
[Exit messenger]
Lady Macduff: Where should I go? I've done no harm.
But that won't save me now.
[Enter murderers]
Who are you?

1st Murderer: Where is your husband?

Lady Macduff: Nowhere, I hope, where men like you can find him.

1st Murderer: Macduff is a traitor.

Boy: My father's not a traitor, wicked man!

1st Murderer: Wicked, am I? Then you'll die too!

[Attacks the boy with a dagger]

Boy: He has killed me, Mother! Run away!

[Exit Lady Macduff, crying 'Murder, murder!']

Act 4, Scene 3

[England. The court of the English King, King Edward. Enter Malcolm and Macduff]

Malcolm: The news you bring from Scotland is so bad,
That we can only cry for our dear country.
Macduff: Let us rather plan to fight.
Every day brings deaths and other horrors.
We have our swords and now's the time to use them.
Malcolm: You've told me many things. Should I believe you?
The tyrant, foul Macbeth, was once thought honest.
You were his friend – he has not harmed you yet.
You may still be the cruel tyrant's friend.
He may have sent you here to spy on me, to learn my thoughts.
Macduff: You must believe me – I am not a traitor.
Malcolm: But Macbeth is. And he's the King.
Even an honest man may feel he must obey
The one who rules him. Why should I trust you?
Satan[76] himself was once an angel. A wicked man
May have an honest face, but honest faces look the same.
Macduff: I have no hope left.
Malcolm: And I have many doubts.
Why did you leave your loved ones in the tyrant's power?
Why did you leave the ones you love in danger?
You left them but you did not say goodbye!
My own safety may depend on you. I must be careful.

Malcolm: *But Macbeth is.*
A good and virtuous nature may recoil
In an imperial charge. But I shall crave your pardon;
That which you are, my thoughts cannot transpose:
Angels are bright still, though the brightest fell:
Though all things foul would wear the brows of grace,

Yet grace must still look so.
Macduff: *I have lost my hopes.*
Malcolm: *Perchance even there*
where I did find my doubts.
Why in that rawness left you wife and child?
Those precious motives, those strong knots of love,
Without leave-taking? I pray you,
Let not my jealousies, be your dishonours,
But mine own safeties: you may be rightly just,
Whatever I shall think.

recoil = give way to
imperial charge = royal command
crave = wish for
transpose = change
brows = foreheads
perchance = perhaps
rawness = unprotected condition
motives = people worthy of love
leave-taking = saying goodbye

Macduff: Bleed, bleed, poor Scotland!
The tyrant's rule will not be stopped by goodness.
Macbeth is safe. Farewell.
I would not be the villain[77] that you think me
For all the riches of the world.
Malcolm: Do not be offended by my words.
I do not fear you, but I weep[78] for Scotland.
As each day passes, so its pains increase.
But I can raise an army, here in England.
Together we shall march against the tyrant
And end his evil rule. But I must tell you this:
Then I shall put my foot upon his head
Or place it on my sword – that may not be the end.
You know Macbeth is cruel and black-hearted.
How do you know I'm not as bad as him,

Or even worse? Take care you don't replace
One tyrant with another.
Macduff: No devil is more wicked than Macbeth.
Malcolm: But I may be. You don't know me at all.
And once I'm King, I can do what I like.
As my power grows, so will my evil nature.
Cruel, lustful[79], greedy[80] – that's what men will call me.
And they will wish Macbeth was still their King.
Macduff: Oh Scotland, Scotland! Oh unhappy country!
If what you say is true, then stay in England.
Oh my poor heart! My hope ends here – farewell.
Malcolm: Good thane, worthy friend, my words were meant to test you.
I feared the tyrant sent you here himself,
To make me join his plans. Nothing that I've said about myself is true.
I'm honest, kind and fair.
In all my life, I've done no harm to anyone.
The only lies I've told are these about myself.
All that I have belongs to you and Scotland.
The English King will give ten thousand men
And with their help, we'll get our country back.
Macduff: Now I can rejoice in Heaven's power!
Brave Malcolm! Great son of your great father.
Together we shall overthrow[81] the tyrant
And make you Scotland's King.
[Enter Ross]
What news from Scotland, worthy thane?
Ross: Alas, poor country! Each day, more people die
And every ear hears cries of pain and fear.
No man in Scotland smiles – they die in pain.
Their lives cut short and ended by the tyrant.
And every minute brings more grief, more awful news.
Macduff: How is my wife?

Ross: Well. She's very well …
Macduff: And all my children?
Ross: Well too.
Macduff: So cruel Macbeth has not disturbed their peace?
Ross: Your family was at peace when I last saw them.
Macduff: Tell us all your news.
Ross: *[To Macduff]* Then know this, noble thane.
The tyrant now has enemies, but yet his power is strong.
You are needed, noble thane, in Scotland.
If you were there, then many men would join you.
The victory would be ours!
Malcolm: Our news is good. Ten thousand Englishmen are ready
To march against the tyrant. Brave Macduff will join us.
Ross: That is great news. I wish that mine were good.
But I have words to say that fill my heart with pain …
Macduff: Please tell us what you mean.
Is this bad news for everyone,
Or is it just for me?
Ross: Forgive me, noble thane, the news I bring is meant for you alone.
Macduff: So I had guessed when you began to speak.
Tell me at once – quickly let me have it.
Ross: You must not blame me for this dreadful news –
The words I have to say are cruel and deadly.
Your castle has been entered by the tyrant's soldiers.
Your wife and children – they have all been killed.
Macduff: My children too?
Ross: Wife, children, servants – all who could be found.
Macduff: I was not there to save them. My wife is killed, you say?
Ross: That's what I said.
Malcolm: Let's use revenge to cure this awful pain!

Macduff: The tyrant has no children and all mine are dead.
All my sweet darlings and their mother too?
Malcolm: You must be strong.
Macduff: And so I shall be, but I must weep too.
They died instead of me. I must be blamed for it.
All that I ask of Heaven is that one day soon
I'll meet the tyrant King and kill him with my sword.
Malcolm: That's what I need to hear. All things are ready.
The angelic powers of Heaven are prepared to help us.
The time has come. Take what cheer you may.
The longest night will always end in day.
[Exit Malcolm, Macduff and Ross]

Act 5, Scene 1

[A room in Macbeth's castle at Dunsinane. Enter a doctor and Lady Macbeth's serving-woman]

Doctor: I have sat here with you for two nights now. Are you sure that Lady Macbeth walks in her sleep?

Woman: Since the King left for battle, my lady has done many strange things. I have seen her get up, put on her night-gown and unlock her cupboard. She takes out some paper and writes a letter, but all this time she is asleep. Then, without waking, she goes back to bed.

Doctor: Her mind must be very troubled. People who walk in their sleep are often ill. I wonder what is troubling her. Does she ever speak? What have you heard her say?

Woman: Words that I dare not repeat, sir.

Doctor: If you tell me, perhaps I can help her.

Woman: No, sir. I was here with her alone. I cannot prove the truth of what I say. You might not believe me.

[Enter Lady Macbeth, carrying a lit candle]

See, she is coming now. And look, sir, she is fast asleep. Watch her, but say nothing.

Doctor: Where did she get the candle from?

Woman: My lady always has a candle in her room at night. It is her order.

Doctor: Look! Her eyes are open.

Woman: But she sees nothing.

[Lady Macbeth puts down the candle. She looks at her hands]

Doctor: What is she doing now? Why is she rubbing her hands together?

Woman: She thinks that she is washing them. She sometimes does that for a quarter of an hour.

Lady Macbeth: No, they are not clean yet. There's still a red spot here.

Doctor: She is speaking! I must write down everything she says.

Lady Macbeth: Yes, just one spot of blood. Oh, that will damn me! Away, damned spot, away! I must wash it off, I must. One, two – the bell strikes and it is time to do it. Oh, Hell is dark – how black it is! For shame, my lord. A soldier who's afraid? Afraid? What for? Who will dare question us? We are too powerful. Yet that old man had so much blood in him, so much blood. I could not believe it.

Lady Macbeth: *Out, damned spot! Out I say! One, two, why, then 'tis time to do it. Hell is murky! Fie, my lord, fie! A soldier and afeard? What need we fear who knows it, when none can call our power to accompt? Yet who would have thought the old man to have had so much blood in him?*

murky = dark, impossible to see through
fie = Shame on you!
afeard = frightened
accompt = account

Doctor: Did you hear that?
Lady Macbeth: The Thane of Fife had a wife. Where is she now? Will I never get my hands clean? That's enough, my lord. Enough of that. You will ruin everything by acting like a coward.
Doctor: Dear, dear. You have known what you should not know.
Woman: She has said things that should be secret. Only Heaven knows all she knows.
Lady Macbeth: The blood's still on my hands. I can smell it! All the sweet perfumes of the East cannot take that smell away. Oh, oh, oh!
Doctor: What a deep sigh. Her heart is very troubled.
Woman: I would not have her troubled heart, even to be a queen.
Doctor: I do not have the skill to cure this illness. But I have known of people who walked in their sleep, but still died peacefully at the end of their lives.

Yes, just one spot of blood. Oh, that will damn me!
Away, damned spot, away! I must wash it off, I must.

Lady Macbeth: Wash your hands. Put on your nightgown. Don't look so afraid. I tell you again. Banquo is in his grave, he cannot come out of it.

Doctor: She speaks of that death too!

Lady Macbeth: To bed, to bed. Someone's knocking at the gate. Come, come, come, give me your hand. What's done cannot be undone. To bed, to bed, to bed!

[Exit Lady Macbeth, with the candle]

Doctor: Will she go back to bed?

Woman: Yes, straight away.

Doctor: Many strange things are being said. Unnatural deeds
Lead to unnatural troubles.
People who are sick in mind, often reveal their secrets.
She needs help from Heaven, not from me.
God, God forgive us all.
Look after her and keep her safe and quiet.
The lady's words have troubled my own heart.
I dare not speak my thoughts. And so, good night.

Woman: Good night, good doctor.

Act 5, Scene 2

[*Scotland. Open land near Dunsinane Castle. The sound of drums.*
Enter Menteith, Angus, Lennox and other thanes – enemies of
Macbeth. They are followed by their armies]

Menteith: The English army's near, led on by Malcolm
And the good Macduff. They come to get revenge.
Their drums are loud enough to cheer the wounded
And to wake the dead.

Angus: Near Birnam Wood we'll meet them.

Menteith: What is Macbeth, the cruel tyrant, doing?

Lennox: He's strengthened his great castle, Dunsinane.
Some say he's mad. Others, who still admire him,
Say anger makes him brave. But all agree
That he has gone too far. He has lost all control.

Angus: And now his secret murders are all known.
And every minute, more men turn against him.
Those who obey him, do so out of fear, not love.
Now the kingly clothes he wears all weigh him down.
He's like a child, wearing a giant's clothes.

Menteith: Who then can be surprised that he shows fear,
When his own heart betrays him?

Angus: *Now does he feel*
His secret murders sticking on his hands;
Now minutely revolts upbraid his faith-breach;
Those he commands move only in command,
Nothing in love: now he feels his title
Hang loose upon him, like a giant's robe
Upon a dwarfish thief.

Menteith: *Who then shall blame*
His pester'd senses to recoil and start,
When all that is within him does condemn
Itself for being there?

minutely = minute by minute
upbraid = criticize
faith-breach = breaking of loyalty
dwarfish = like a very small person who will never grow to average size
pester'd = troubled
start = make a sudden movement
condemn = blame

Angus: Well, let's march on and all give our support
To young Prince Malcolm. He's our rightful lord.
We're here to cure our country's sickness, and we will.
Lennox: We'll save the good and cut out all that's bad.
Now let's march on to Birnam!

Act 5, Scene 3

[Inside Macbeth's castle at Dunsinane. Enter Macbeth and the doctor]

Macbeth: Bring no more news!
What do I care, if all men turn against me?
Till Birnam Wood moves on to Dunsinane
I have no need to fear. Malcolm is just a boy
And he was born as all men are. The spirits
Whom the three sisters called, said this to me:
'No man of woman born shall harm Macbeth.'
Then leave me, you false thanes
And join the easy-living Englishmen.
The brave heart and mind that keep me here
Shall never faint with doubt nor shake with fear.
[Enter servant. His face is full of fear]
Servant: There are ten thousand soldiers, sir.
Macbeth: What soldiers, fool?
Damn you, you coward! Those milk-white cheeks of yours
Make everyone afraid. What soldiers, milk-face?
Servant: The English army, sir.
Macbeth: Get out!
[Exit servant. Macbeth calls for Seyton]
Seyton! Oh, I feel sick at heart when I see such ...
Seyton, where are you? This latest move against me
Will either keep me happy on my throne,
Or push me from it. I have lived long enough.
I am like a dry and yellow leaf, ready to fall.
And the expected blessings of old age, like honour,
Love, respect and many friends, I cannot hope to have.
But in their place are whispered curses, flattering lies
And service given against the servant's will.
Seyton!
[Enter Seyton]

Macbeth: *Take thy face hence.*
[Exit servant]
Seyton, I am sick at heart,
When I behold: Seyton, I say, this push
Will cheer me ever, or disseat me now.
I have liv'd long enough: my way of life
Is fall'n into the sere, the yellow leaf,
And that which should accompany old age,
As honour, love, obedience, troops of friends,
I must not look to have; but in their stead,
Curses, not loud but deep, mouth-honour, breath
Which the poor heart would fain deny and dare not.
Seyton!

push = final effort
disseat = unseat me from my throne
sere = dry, withered
troops of = large numbers of
mouth-honour = insincere respect
fain = want to

Seyton: Yes, my gracious King?
Macbeth: Any more news?
Seyton: The last report was true, my noble lord.
Macbeth: I'll fight until my flesh[82] is all cut from me.
Give me my armour.
Seyton: It's not needed yet.
Macbeth: I want to put it on.
Send out more men on horses. See what's going on.
Hang all those cowards who say they are afraid.
Bring me my armour.
[To the doctor] How is your patient, doctor?
Doctor: She is not sick in body, but in mind. She is disturbed
By many troubling thoughts that keep her from her rest.
Macbeth: Oh, cure her of that.
Don't you have medicine for a mind that's sick?

Something to dull sad memories and clear the mind
Of deep and fearful thoughts.
Perhaps you have some pleasant drug that takes away
The deep depression that drags down mind and feelings?
Doctor: I'm afraid the patient must do that for herself.
[Seyton returns with Macbeth's armour and begins to dress him in it]
Macbeth: Throw medicine to the dogs, I'll do without it.
Come, put my armour on, give me my spear.
Get my men ready, Seyton. The thanes are leaving, doctor.
If you could find my country's sickness, doctor
And with your cleansing drugs bring it to health again
My praise of you would echo round the world.
[To Seyton] Pull off that piece of armour.
[Then to the doctor]
What medicine could you use to get rid of the English?
Have you heard they're here, good doctor?
Doctor: Yes, my good lord. Your preparations make that clear to
us.
Macbeth: Seyton, bring that piece of armour after me.
Death and destruction cannot make me fear
Till Birnam Wood is moved and finds me here!
[Exit Macbeth and Seyton with his armour]
Doctor: If I could leave this cursed Dunsinane
Nothing on earth would bring me here again!
[Exit]

Act 5, Scene 4

[Enter Malcolm, Macduff, Lennox, Ross, several thanes, English lords and their armies, which are led by Siward]

Malcolm: My friends, I hope the day will soon be here
When we can all live safely in our homes.
This wood in front of us, what is it called?

Lennox: It is the wood of Birnam, my good lord.

Malcolm: Let every soldier cut himself a branch
To carry, as he marches. Then they can hide themselves
As they move forward.
No one will see how big our army is, or where it is.
And all reports about us will be false.

Lennox: It shall be done.

Siward: Macbeth, the cruel tyrant, is still in Dunsinane,
His strongest castle. If we besiege⁸³ it,
He could stay in safety and defy our armies.

Malcolm: That is his best hope. Many of his men have left.
Those still in Dunsinane must stay there.
They serve him now in fear and not with love.

Macduff: We hope those reports are true. Now we must make
Our plans to end the tyrant's rule.

Siward: The size of both our armies will decide the outcome.
We cannot judge the loyalty of Macbeth's men.
Nothing is certain till the final battle.
Let us prepare for that.

Act 5, Scene 5

[In the courtyard of Dunsinane castle. Enter Macbeth and Seyton]
Macbeth: Hang all our flags on the high castle walls.
Reports say that their armies are advancing,
What do I care?
The castle is too strong to be destroyed.
Hunger and sickness will destroy their soldiers,
Before they take strong Dunsinane.
If all my Scottish soldiers had been loyal,
We could have fought the English, face to face
And driven them from Scotland.
[The sound of women crying] What is that noise?
Seyton: The sound of crying women, my good lord.
[Exit Seyton]
Macbeth: I have forgotten what it means to be afraid.
Not long ago, a cry at night would freeze my blood –
My hair would stand on end.
But I have seen and heard such evil things
Now nothing frightens me.
[Enter Seyton]
What was the reason for that cry?
Seyton: The Queen, my lord, has killed herself.
Macbeth: She had to die sometime, I suppose.
There would have been a time to talk of death.
Tomorrow, and tomorrow, and tomorrow,
Day follows day with slow and tired steps
Until time ends. And all our days have shown fools
The way to death, when all things end in dust.
Blow out the candle – life's shadow disappears.
The shadow of an actor who, for an hour,
Tries to pretend that what he does is real.
And then his voice is heard no more.
A man's life is like a story, told badly by a fool,

Whose shouts and strong words make it seem important.
But it means nothing.

Macbeth: *She should have died hereafter;*
There would have been a time for such a word:
Tomorrow, and tomorrow, and tomorrow
Creeps in this petty pace from day to day,
To the last syllable of recorded time;
And all our yesterdays have lighted fools
The way to dusty death. Out, out, brief candle!
Life's but a walking shadow, a poor player
That struts and frets his hour upon the stage,
And then is heard no more: It is a tale
Told by an idiot, full of sound and fury,
Signifying nothing.

hereafter = in the future
petty = short
pace = step
syllable = a sound, part of a word
struts = walks proudly
frets = worries about
signifying = meaning

[Enter messenger]
More news? Then tell it quickly!
Messenger: My gracious lord, I come to tell you what I saw.
I don't know what to say.
Macbeth: Tell me at once.
Messenger: As I stood at watch upon the hill,
I looked towards Birnam. And then it seemed to me,
The wood began to move.
Macbeth: Liar and traitor!
Messenger: If I do not speak the truth, then you
should be angry.
See for yourself, the wood is moving nearer.

Macbeth: If you are lying, I'll hang you from a tree
Until you die of hunger. If your report is true,
I don't care if you hang me up instead.
I feel my courage weaken and I begin
To doubt those devilish lies that sound like truth.
'Macbeth shall never be defeated till
Great Birnam Wood to high Dunsinane Hill
Shall move against him.'
That's what the spirit said. And now the wood
Is moving on towards me.
To arms! To arms! We must go out and fight!
If what he says is true, there's no escape,
Whether I go or stay. I am already tired of life.
The world itself could end, for all I care.
Ring the alarm bell! Though the future's black
At least we'll die with armour on our back!
[Macbeth and his soldiers leave the castle to fight]

Act 5, Scene 6

[Dunsinane. A short distance from the castle gate. Enter Malcolm, Macduff, Siward and the Scottish and English armies. The sound of trumpets and drums]

Malcolm: Stop. We are near enough.

[To his soldiers]

Throw down your leafy branches. Show yourselves as men.
My noble uncle Siward, you and your good son
Will lead the first attack. Macduff and myself
Will be behind you. When the time is right,
Our soldiers will move forward to support you.

Siward: May luck go with you, my good Malcolm.
We must take on the tyrant's power tonight.
We shall be beaten, if we fail to fight.

Macduff: Blow all our trumpets, give them all your breath
To call all men to battle, blood and death!

[The armies move forward, to the sound of trumpets]

Act 5, Scene 7

[Macbeth comes out from Dunsinane castle]
Macbeth: I am like a bear, tied to a stake[84] and made to fight.
Where's the man not born of woman?
I must fear only him – no other one.
[Enter Young Siward, Siward's son]
Young Siward: What is your name?
Macbeth: You'd be afraid to hear it.
Young Siward: No. Even though your name is hotter than
The name of any devil burning in the fires of Hell.
Macbeth: My name's Macbeth.
Young Siward: The Devil himself could not say a name
I hated more.
Macbeth: Or were more afraid to hear!
Young Siward: I'll prove that is not true, you hated tyrant!
I'll prove it with my sword!
[They fight and Young Siward is killed]
Macbeth: The spirits told the truth. No man has power
Enough to kill me. You cannot do me harm,
You were of woman born – so said the witches' charm.
[Exit Macbeth. The sound of more fighting. Enter Macduff]
Macduff: The sound of fighting is much louder here.
Tyrant, show your face!
If you are killed, but by another man,
The ghosts of my dead wife and my dear children
Will never leave me. I have made up my mind.
I will kill no more, until I find the tyrant.
I hear the sound of fighting louder still.
I feel Macbeth is near. Let me find him, Heaven!
That is all I ask.
[Exit Macduff. Enter Malcolm and Siward]
Siward: This way, my lord. Great Dunsinane is yours.
Many of the tyrant's men have left him.

They fight with us, beside your worthy thanes.
In a short time, the victory will be yours.
Malcolm: The tyrant's men have fought beside me too.
Siward: Noble sir, enter your royal castle!
[Malcolm and Siward enter Dunsinane Castle]

Act 5, Scene 8

[Outside the castle. Enter Macbeth]
Macbeth: I have lost, but why should I give up?
Defeated Roman leaders used to kill themselves,
But I shall not do that.
While one man is alive, I'll kill him first.
[Enter Macduff]
Macduff: Turn and face me, hound[85] of Hell!
Macbeth: You are the last man whom I want to fight.
I have done your family too much harm already.
Macduff: My answer's in my sword, not in my words.
Your evil is beyond words, you bloody villain!
[They fight]
Macbeth: Fighting me is useless.
You might as well fight air, as try to wound me.
You had better use your sword on other men –
Men who your sword can kill. I cannot die.
I am protected by the charm that said:
'No man of woman born shall harm Macbeth.'
Macduff: That charm is useless. The devilish angel
Whom you still serve must tell you this:
Macduff was cut early from his mother's side
And not born in the natural way at all.

Macbeth: *Thou losest labour.*
As easy mayst thou the intrenchant air
With thy keen sword impress, as make me bleed:
Let fall thy blade on vulnerable crests,
I bear a charmed life, which must not yield
To one of woman born.
Macduff: *Despair thy charm,*
And let the Angel whom thou still hast serv'd

> *Tell thee, Macduff was from his mother's womb*
> *Untimely ripp'd.*
>
> labour = effort
> *intrenchant* = unable to be cut
> keen = sharp
> *impress* = cut, wound
> vulnerable = able to be hurt
> crests = helmets, heads (of soldiers)
> womb = the part of a woman where a baby develops
> untimely = before the right time
> *ripp'd* = torn

Macbeth: Cursed is the man who tells me so.
His words have killed my courage.
Those double-dealing spirits made a fool of me
With their dishonest words. They promised hope,
Then took that hope away. I will not fight with you.
Macduff: Then you must yield[86], you coward.
You will be put on show as all strange monsters are.
Your painted picture will be fixed upon a stake
With these words written under it:
'Here you can see Macbeth, the once-feared monster-tyrant.'
Macbeth: I will not yield and kiss the ground
Before young Malcolm's feet. Nor will I
Allow myself to be cursed and laughed at
By the noisy crowd.
Yes, Birnam Wood has come to Dunsinane
You were not born of woman – yet I'll fight.
My shield will still protect me. Come on, Macduff!
Damned be the man who first cries 'Stop! Enough!'
[They fight for some time and, at last, Macbeth is killed]

You were not born of woman – yet I'll fight.

Act 5, Scene 9

[Inside the castle. Drums are heard. Enter Malcolm, Siward, Ross, thanes and soldiers]

Malcolm: Some friends are not here yet. I hope they're safe.

Siward: Some men had to die, but many more remain.
Our victory's been won without great loss.

Malcolm: Macduff is missing, and your noble son.

Ross: *[To Siward]*
Your son, my lord, has given up his life.
That life was short, but yet he was a man.
And showed himself to be a worthy soldier.
He stood his ground, fought bravely as a man.
And like a man, he died.

Siward: Then you are sure he's dead?

Ross: Yes, he is dead. He was such a worthy son
That your unhappiness could last for ever.
But it must not.

Siward: Was he wounded from the front?

Ross: Yes, sir, he was.

Siward: Then he was worthy to be God's soldier
And had a worthy death. I'll mourn[87] for him a little
And there's an end. The mourning bell sounds for him.
That is enough.

Malcolm: I'll add my mourning too, for he deserves it.

Siward: I cannot mourn for ever. As he died well,
My only sign of grief will be his mourning bell.
So God be with him! But here is something better!

[Enter Macduff, with Macbeth's head on a spear]

Macduff: *[Speaking to Malcolm]*
Hail, Malcolm, King of Scotland, hail!
Here is the cursed tyrant's head. Now we are free.
You are surrounded by these worthy thanes
Who all confirm that you are now their King.

Hail, King of Scotland!

Let them repeat with me: Hail, King of Scotland!
All: Hail, King of Scotland!
[The sound of trumpets]
Malcolm: My loyal friends, you will be rewarded very soon.
My thanes and relatives, I name you earls[88].
This is the highest honour I can give.
Friends who have fled the tyrant's power,
Will be called back home to Scotland.
Those men who served this butcher and his evil Queen,
Will soon be found and punished.
The Queen herself, I hear, has died by her own hand.
We shall put all things right, by Heaven's grace,
And in good time, make this a blessed place.
So thanks to all – to each and every one,
Whom we invite, to see us crowned at Scone!
[Cheers, trumpets and drums. All march away]

Points for Understanding

Act 1

1   What were we told about Macbeth's character and actions before we met him?
2   What did the three witches say about the futures of Macbeth and Banquo?
3   Describe how Macbeth and Banquo reacted to the witches' information.
4   In this act, Lady Macbeth seemed to have a stronger character than her husband. Give some examples that suggest this is true.
5   Macbeth thought of several reasons for not killing King Duncan. Say what these reasons were.
6   How did Lady Macbeth persuade her husband to commit the murder?

Act 2

1   Banquo was unhappy at the beginning of this act. Why?
2   What did Macbeth think that he saw before he committed the murder?
3   Describe how Duncan's dead body was discovered.
4   How did the following people react to the King's death?
    (a) Macduff   (b) Malcolm and Donalbain   (c) Macbeth
    (d) Lady Macbeth
5   What reason did Macbeth give for killing Duncan's servants? What do you think his real reason was?
6   In your opinion, did Lady Macbeth really faint or was she acting? Give reasons for your answer.
7   Malcolm was King Duncan's eldest son and heir. Why was Macbeth made king?

Act 3

1. Banquo believed that the three witches could foretell the future. How had their words already affected Macbeth and himself?
2. Macbeth decided that Banquo must be murdered. Why was that necessary?
3. Macbeth did not tell his wife about this murder. Why do you think he decided not to do this?
4. Banquo's son, Fleance, escaped. Why was Macbeth so unhappy about that?
5. If you were producing the play, would you have an actor come on stage as Banquo's ghost or not? Give reasons for your answer.
6. Macbeth made a decision at the end of this act. What was it?
7. This decision showed that Macbeth had changed. In what way had he changed?
8. People now suspected Macbeth of many murders. Who had decided to bring Macbeth's rule to an end and how did they plan to do it?

Act 4

1. Why did Macbeth go to see the three witches again?
2. What were the witches doing when Macbeth found them?
3. The witches' masters told Macbeth about his future. Why was Macbeth reassured by what they said?
4. After seeing the three spirits, Macbeth asked the witches a question. What was this question?
5. Why was Macbeth horrified by what he saw next?
6. Why was Lady Macduff so angry with her husband in the second scene?
7. In your opinion, why did Macduff leave his family unprotected in Scotland?
8. Why did Malcolm tell Macduff lies about himself?
9. What did Macduff pray for?

Act 5

1   Most of Lady Macbeth's sleep-walking scene was written in prose[89], not blank verse. Can you suggest why?
2   Macbeth's enemies were marching towards Dunsinane, but he still had hope. Why was that?
3   What happened to Lady Macbeth and why?
4   How did Macbeth react when he heard the news about Birnam Wood?
5   When did Macbeth finally realize that the witches had lied to him?
6   What were your feelings about Macbeth at the end of the play?

Glossary

1 **influenced** – *to influence someone* (page 6)
   to affect the way that someone thinks or behaves, or to affect the way
   that something happens
2 **manuscript** (page 6)
   a writer's original pages of a book, article or document before it is
   published
3 **treason** (page 6)
   the crime of helping your country's enemies or of trying to destroy
   your country's government
4 **retired** – *to retire* (page 6)
   to stop working, especially when you reach the age when you are
   officially too old to work
5 **fate** (page 7)
   the things that happen to someone, especially unpleasant things
6 **unrest** (page 7)
   angry or violent behaviour by people who are protesting against
   something
7 **throne** – *to be on the throne* (page 7)
   to be in the position of being a king or queen
8 **parliament** (page 7)
   an official elected group of people in some countries who meet to
   make the laws of the country and discuss national issues
9 **executed** – *to execute someone* (page 7)
   to kill someone as a punishment for a crime
10 **flatter** (page 7)
   to praise someone in order to get something that you want, especially
   in a way that is not sincere
11 **tyrant** (page 8)
   someone who rules a country in a cruel and unfair way
12 **supernatural** (page 8)
   used about things that seem to come from a power such as magic and
   do not have a natural or scientific explanation
13 **ambition** (page 8)
   the feeling that you want very much to become successful, rich,
   famous etc is called *ambition*. An *ambitious* person is determined to
   be successful, rich, famous etc.
14 **dreadful** (page 8)
   very unpleasant

15 **foretell** (page 9)
to say what will happen in the future
16 **spell** (page 9)
words or actions that are intended to make magic things happen
17 **cheer** (page 10)
a feeling of happiness. Someone or something that makes you feel happy because of being pleasant or enjoyable is *cheerful*. A *cheer* is a loud shout of happiness or approval.
18 **thane** (page 12)
in English history, a man who was given land in exchange for fighting for the king or another important person
19 **heath** (page 13)
a wide area of wild land where only rough grass and bushes grow
20 **foul** (page 13)
evil, very bad or unpleasant. *Foul* weather is very unpleasant, with rain, snow or wind.
21 **rebel** (page 13)
someone who tries to remove a government or leader using force
22 **wicked** (page 13)
morally wrong and deliberately intending to hurt people
23 **traitor** (page 13)
someone who is not loyal to their friends, family, employer or country
24 **blow** (page 13)
a hard hit from someone's hand or an object
25 **alarmed** (page 14)
frightened or worried that something unpleasant or dangerous might happen
26 **hare** (page 14)
an animal similar to a rabbit, but with a bigger body and longer ears and legs, that can run very fast
27 **gracious** (page 14)
showing kindness and good manners
28 **assisted** – *to assist someone* (page 14)
to help someone or something
29 **blest** – *to bless someone* (page 15)
if God blesses someone or something, he helps and protects them
30 **drowned** – *to drown* (page 15)
to sink under water and die

31 **homeward** (page 15)
in the direction of home
32 **hail** (page 16)
to say publicly how good or important someone or something is
33 **crown** (page 20)
to make someone a king or queen during a ceremony in which a crown is put on their head
34 **worthy** (page 21)
a *worthy* person or thing has qualities that make people respect them. In old English it was used as a form of address.
35 **confessed** – *to confess something* (page 22)
to admit that you have committed a crime or done something wrong
36 **nobly** (page 22)
in an honest and brave way that other people admire. A person who behaves in this way is *noble*.
37 **duty** (page 22)
a legal or moral obligation
38 **deed** (page 22)
something that someone does
39 **heir** (page 22)
someone who will receive money, property or a title when another person dies
40 **desire** (page 24)
to want something
41 **bold** (page 24)
confident and not afraid of people
42 **glory** (page 27)
admiration and praise that you get because you have done something impressive
43 **hostess** (page 28)
a woman who invites someone to a meal or party, or to stay for a short time in her home. A man who does this is called a *host*.
44 **feast** (page 29)
a large meal for a lot of people, usually in order to celebrate something
45 **revenge** (page 29)
something that you do to hurt or punish someone because they have hurt you or someone else

46 **plead** (page 29)
to ask for something in an urgent or emotional way
47 **angelic** (page 29)
an *angelic* voice is very beautiful, like the voice of an *angel* – a spirit
that in some religions is believed to live in Heaven with God
48 **spur** (page 29)
something that encourages someone to do something
49 **praise** (page 30)
to express strong approval or admiration for someone or something,
especially in public
50 **coward** (page 30)
someone who is not brave enough to fight or do something difficult
or dangerous that they should do
51 **dagger** (page 30)
a weapon like a very small sword
52 **grief** (page 30)
a strong feeling of sadness, usually because someone has died
53 **mischief** (page 33)
trouble or disagreement that someone deliberately causes
54 **betray** (page 33)
to show something or give a sign of something
55 **sacred** (page 40)
considered to be holy or connected with God in a special way
56 **curse** (page 45)
to say or think offensive or impolite words about someone or
something
57 **coronation** (page 45)
a ceremony at which someone officially becomes king or queen
58 **tormented** – *to torment someone* (page 50)
to make someone suffer severe physical or mental pain, often
deliberately
59 **grave** (page 50)
the place where a dead body is buried in a deep hole in the ground
60 **toast** (page 54)
an occasion when people all drink together and say someone's name
in order to express their admiration or their good wishes
61 **ditch** (page 54)
a long narrow hole dug along the side of a road or field, usually so
that water can run into it

62 **absence** (page 55)

a period of time when someone is not where they should be or where they usually are

63 **revealed** – *to reveal something* (page 59)

to let something become known, for example a secret or information that was previously not known

64 **treachery** (page 60)

the behaviour of someone who pretends that they support you but secretly tries to harm you, for example by helping an enemy

65 **fled** – *to flee* (page 61)

to escape from a dangerous situation or place very quickly

66 **cauldron** (page 62)

a large round metal pot usually used for cooking over a fire

67 **toad** (page 62)

a small animal that is similar to a frog but has brown skin and lives mainly on land

68 **slimy** (page 62)

covered with a thick wet unpleasant substance

69 **jaw** (page 62)

the part of your mouth where your teeth grow

70 **pricking** – *to prick* (page 62)

to experience a sharp stinging feeling or to cause this feeling on someone's skin or eyes

71 **seek** (page 63)

to ask for something or to try to get something

72 **crop** (page 63)

a plant grown for food, usually on a farm

73 **haunt** (page 65)

if a place is *haunted* by the spirit of a dead person, some people believe that the spirit appears there

74 **grieve** (page 66)

to upset someone

75 **damned** (page 67)

if someone is *damned*, they are sent to *Hell*. According to some religions, *Hell* is the place where bad people are sent to suffer for ever when they die, because of the bad things that they have done.

76 **Satan** (page 71)

the most powerful evil spirit in many religions such as Christianity, Islam and Judaism

77 **villain** (page 72)
an evil person or a criminal
78 **weep** (page 72)
to cry because you feel unhappy or have some other strong emotion
79 **lustful** (page 73)
full of passionate feeling
80 **greedy** (page 73)
wanting more money, things or power than you need
81 **overthrow** (page 73)
to force a leader or government out of their position of power
82 **flesh** (page 83)
the soft part of people's or animals' bodies that consists mostly of muscle and fat
83 **besiege** (page 85)
to surround a place with an army and prevent the people there from getting food and supplies, as a way of getting control of it
84 **stake** (page 90)
a wooden or metal post with a pointed end that is used for supporting or marking something
85 **hound** (page 92)
a dog
86 **yield** (page 93)
to finally agree to do what someone else wants you to do
87 **mourn** (page 95)
to feel extremely sad because someone has died, and to express this in public
88 **earl** (page 97)
a man with a very high social position in the UK
89 **prose** (page 100)
written language in its ordinary form, as opposed to poetry

Definitions adapted from the Macmillan English Dictionary *2nd Edition* © *Macmillan Publishers Ltd 2007*
www.macmillandictionaries.com

Exercises

Background Information

Circle the correct information to complete the sentences.

1 Shakespeare was born in the <u>15th</u> / (16th) century.

2 Shakespeare's father was a <u>rich</u> / <u>poor</u> businessman.

3 Shakespeare had a good <u>school</u> / <u>university</u> education.

4 Shakespeare had <u>two</u> / <u>three</u> children.

5 Shakespeare lived in London for about <u>twenty</u> / <u>thirty</u> years.

6 There were <u>few</u> / <u>many</u> theatres in London at the time.

7 Shakespeare <u>wrote all new plays</u> / <u>changed old plays</u>.

8 *Macbeth* was the last <u>tragic</u> / <u>funny</u> play written by Shakespeare.

9 The political situation was <u>good</u> / <u>difficult</u> at the time.

10 *Macbeth* had to make <u>the people</u> / <u>the King</u> happy.

11 King James <u>believed</u> / <u>didn't believe</u> in the supernatural.

12 Blank verse is a <u>rhyming</u> / <u>non-rhyming</u> style of writing.

13 Shorter sentences often show <u>positive</u> / <u>negative</u> emotions.

14 Rhyming couplets create a <u>dramatic</u> / <u>calm</u> feeling.

People in the Story

Write a name or names next to the correct information below. You can use the names more than once.

> Malcolm   Macduff   Macbeth   Lady Macbeth
> Three witches   Donalbain   Banquo

1	*Three witches*	told Macbeth his future titles.
2		encouraged Macbeth to kill Duncan.
3		escaped to England and Ireland because they were afraid.
4		became King after Duncan had been murdered.
5		appeared as a ghost after he had been murdered.
6		fought together against Macbeth.
7		ended her own life.
8		used trees to hide the army's approach.
9		killed Macbeth.
10		was heir to the throne and became King of Scotland.

True or False?

Read the statements about *Macbeth*. Write T (True) or F (False).

1	Macbeth and Banquo were good friends at the beginning.	T
2	The witches said Banquo's sons would be kings.	
3	Lady Macbeth thought her husband was brave.	
4	Lady Macbeth killed Duncan's servants.	
5	Macbeth was haunted by the ghost of Banquo.	
6	The witches' second three predictions made Macbeth afraid.	
7	Lady Macduff thought her husband was dead.	
8	Macduff's family was killed.	
9	Lady Macbeth did not feel guilty about the murder of the King.	
10	Lady Macbeth imagined blood on her hands.	
11	Malcolm and Menteith led the English army.	
12	Macbeth's soldiers were loyal to him at the end.	
13	Siward's son was killed by Macbeth.	
14	Macduff was not born in a natural way.	
15	King Malcolm gave his loyal friends a new title.	

Multiple Choice

Tick the best answers. Sometimes there is more than one answer.

1 What did Lennox and Ross realize?
   a That Macbeth had murdered Duncan and Banquo. ✓
   b That Macbeth had killed Macduff.
   c That Macbeth had murdered the English King.
   d That Macbeth had killed Duncan's servants to hide the truth. ✓

2 What did the witches tell Macbeth?
   a To be afraid of Macduff.
   b That he should not be afraid of any man born from woman.
   c That his sons would be kings.
   d That he would be in danger if the wood started moving.

3 What did Ross tell Lady Macduff?
   a That Macduff was a traitor.
   b That Macduff was dead.
   c That Macduff had good reasons for leaving.
   d That the murderers were coming for her.

4 What did Lady Macbeth do when she became ill?
   a Walk in her sleep.
   b Carry a candle.
   c Wash her hands.
   d Wear perfume.

5 What news did Lennox give the thanes about Macbeth?
   a That he had lost control.
   b That he was extremely angry.
   c That he had a large army.
   d That he had changed for the better.

6 How did Macbeth feel when he heard about his wife's death?
   a Very frightened.
   b Depressed.
   c Pleased.
   d He didn't care.

Vocabulary: Anagrams

Write the letters in the correct order to make words from the play.

1	ORTARIT	*traitor*	someone who is not loyal to a king or queen
2	TAFE		a power that decides what will happen
3	YARNTT		someone who has complete power and uses it in a bad way
4	ETELFORL		to predict the future
5	LOFU		very very bad
6	AIOCSGRU		to behave in a polite, calm way
7	EDED		an action (formal)
8	TONHER		the position of being a king or queen
9	BENOL		good, honest and brave
10	REHI		someone who will receive money, possessions or a position after another person's death
11	STEFA		a large meal, usually for a special occasion
12	DAPLE		to ask for something in an emotional way
13	AEGRV		a place in the ground to put dead people
14	KECDIW		something that is very bad and morally wrong
15	WONRD		to die in water

Words from the Story

Complete the gaps. Use each word in the box once. You may need to change the form of the verbs.

~~treason~~	hail	bold	hostess	revenge	coward	mischief
	betray	torment	haunt	mourn	praise	

1 The Thane of Cawdor was not loyal to the King. He had committed
   ......*treason*........ .

2 Lady Macbeth was .... by the guilt she felt.

3 Macbeth was .... by the ghost of Banquo.

4 Malcolm wanted to find and kill his father's murderer. He wanted
   ....

5 Lady Macbeth gave the King and his sons wine and good food. She was
   a good ....

6 Lady Macbeth thought Macbeth was weak and called him a
   ....

7 The witches wanted to cause problems for people. They caused
   ....

8 Macduff's family were killed, but he did not have much time to
   .... their deaths.

9 Macbeth was greeted as a hero at the beginning of the story and later
   .... as King of Scotland.

10 In order to commit the murder, Macbeth needed to have courage and
   be ....

11 Macbeth was given a lot of .... for defeating King
   Duncan's enemies.

12 Duncan believed in Macbeth, but Macbeth .... him.

Word Focus

Complete the table with the missing words. The missing words are all in the play.

NOUN	ADJECTIVE	VERB
1 *bravery*	brave	
confession		2
3	courageous	
grief		4
5	ambitious	
flattery		6
execution		7
8	glorious	
angel	9	
greed	10	
blood	11	bleed
12	guilty	

Complete the sentences with one of the words from the table. You may need to change the form of the verbs.

Lady Macbeth had great ¹ .... *ambition* .... for herself and her husband. She became very ² .... and wanted more and more power for Macbeth. She called her husband a coward, saying he had no ³ .... However, King Duncan thought she was a ⁴ .... hostess. Lady Macbeth made him feel good and ⁵ .... him. After the murder, she began to feel ⁶ .... and imagined ⁷ .... on her hands.

113

Duncan thought that Macbeth and Banquo were [8]............................. and
[9]............................. soldiers when they won the battle. Until Macbeth met
the witches, he did not have dreams of being King and wasn't so
[10]............................. . He murdered Duncan and killed the King's servants
before they could deny their [11]............................. . Macbeth almost
[12]............................. to the murder, but then he went on to commit more
murders.

Pronunciation: Vowel sounds

Circle the word which has a different vowel sound.

1	d<u>u</u>ty	exec<u>u</u>te	(g<u>ui</u>lty)	tr<u>u</u>th
2	<u>a</u>ctor	c<u>a</u>ndle	d<u>ay</u>	d<u>a</u>gger
3	m<u>ou</u>rn	l<u>or</u>d	st<u>o</u>ry	sh<u>ou</u>t
4	h<u>ou</u>r	s<u>ou</u>nd	gl<u>o</u>ry	f<u>ou</u>l
5	fl<u>a</u>tter	c<u>a</u>stle	<u>a</u>rmy	al<u>a</u>rm
6	bl<u>oo</u>d	s<u>o</u>ldier	d<u>u</u>st	l<u>u</u>stful
7	c<u>o</u>ward	n<u>o</u>ble	h<u>o</u>stess	thr<u>o</u>ne
8	gr<u>a</u>ve	tr<u>ai</u>tor	<u>ea</u>rl	h<u>ai</u>l
9	gr<u>ie</u>ve	fl<u>e</u>sh	h<u>ea</u>th	w<u>ee</u>p

Grammar: The third conditional active and passive

Write the sentences in the third conditional active or passive form using the verbs in brackets.

> **Example 1** If Macbeth _hadn't met_ (meet) the witches, he _wouldn't have had_ (have) the idea of killing the King.
>
> **Example 2** If Macbeth _had been_ (be) stronger, he _wouldn't have been persuaded_ (persuade) to kill Duncan.

1 If the King .... (look) like Lady Macbeth's father, she .... (kill) him.

2 If Macbeth .... (name) King, he .... (be) safe.

3 If Macbeth .... (listen) to his wife, he .... (murder) Duncan.

4 If Duncan's servants .... (execute), they .... (be able) to tell the truth.

5 If Malcolm .... (go) to England, he .... (be) in danger.

6 Lady Macbeth .... (start) sleepwalking if she .... (feel) guilty.

7 If Lady Macbeth .... (go) mad, she .... (commit) suicide.

8 Malcolm and Macduff .... (beat) if they .... (have) so much support.

9 Malcolm .... (make) King if he .... (defeat) Macbeth.

10 Macbeth .... (become) a tyrant if he .... (listen) to the witches.

Making Questions

Write subject or object questions. The underlined information in the answers will help you.

Example 1	*What did the witches promise Macbeth?* The witches promised Macbeth <u>that he would receive three titles</u>.	
Example 2	*Who was with Macbeth when he met the witches?* <u>Banquo</u> was with Macbeth when he met the witches.	

Q1

A1   <u>The Thane of Cawdor</u> was a traitor.

Q2

A2   Macbeth met the witches <u>on the heath</u>.

Q3

A3   <u>Duncan and his sons</u> went to stay at Macbeth's castle.

Q4

A4   Lady Macbeth called her husband <u>a coward</u>.

Q5

A5   <u>Macbeth's wife</u> persuaded him to commit the murder.

Q6

A6   Macbeth used <u>a dagger</u> to kill Duncan.

Q7

A7   <u>The weather was stormy</u> on the night of the murder.

Q8

A8   Macbeth and his wife blamed <u>the servants</u> for the murder.

Q9

A9   Malcolm escaped to England <u>because he thought he was in danger</u>.

Q10

A10 <u>Banquo</u> thought Macbeth was guilty.

Q11

A11 Macbeth's coronation was <u>in Scone</u>.

Q12

A12 Macbeth saw <u>Banquo's ghost</u> at the feast.

Q13

A13 <u>The doctor</u> felt troubled after his visit to Macbeth's castle.

Q14

A14 There were about <u>ten thousand English soldiers</u> outside Macbeth's castle.

Q15

A15 <u>Macduff</u> killed Macbeth.

Macmillan Readers

www.macmillanenglish.com/readers

Welcome to Macmillan Readers Online

This website contains both support material for teachers to use in class, as well as a wealth of resources written for students, to accompany their language learning.

Please click on the links below to visit the student website, or the **Macmillan Readers** resource site for teachers.

Teachers   **Students**

- **Students' section** featuring *The Book Corner Club*, for those students who want to study Readers in a book club. It also features tips for creative writing and essays, a level test, webquests and URLs for further reading, articles, interviews with authors, audio, poetry and author biography worksheets
- **Teachers' section** with expanded collection of free support material including worksheets, answer keys, sample chapters, sample audio, webquests, author data sheets and the *Using Graded Readers in the Classroom* guide

Macmillan Education
4 Crinan Street
London N1 9XW
A division of Macmillan Publishers Limited
Companies and representatives throughout the world

ISBN 978–0–2304–0221–8
ISBN 978–0–2304–0223–2 (with CD edition)

This version of *Macbeth* was retold by Margaret Tarner for
Macmillan Readers.

First published 2010
Text © Macmillan Publishers Limited 2010
Design and illustration © Macmillan Publishers Limited 2010
This version first published 2010

Illustrated by Sharif Tarabay
Cover photograph by The Kobal Collection/Columbia

Printed and bound in Thailand

without CD edition
2017   2016   2015
12   11   10   9   8   7

with CD edition
2018   2017   2016
11   10   9   8   7   6